A Collectors

COLOUR BOX
TEDDY BEARS

John Hughes

Published in the United Kingdom
by
Collectables Publishing Limited

ACKNOWLEDGMENTS

Many thanks to the following people:
Frances and Peter Fagan for their cooperation and enthusiasm
for the project, for permission to reproduce copyright text
from a variety of printed sources, and for proofing
and correcting the manuscript;
Everyone at Bronze Age Limited who provided information,
in particular Liz Bernard, Pam Ellison, Terry Fairbairn, Vera Huber,
Pat Glass, Hazel Gryczka, Pat Learmonth, Cairen McAulay,
Margaret Smith and Joan Walker-Alton;
Penny Davies of Ronn Ballantyne Photographic for extensive
use of existing photography;
Glenn Blackman for design and original photography;
Myra Whellans for details about the early days at Bronze Age Limited;
The numerous collectors and dealers who provided
information — Roger Boylan, Kathleen Cook, Lynda Gould,
Ann Macfarlane, the Marks family, Morna Reeves,
Arild Soloest, Carrie Sterk.

Thanks also to Peter Gilardi of The Grange, Lauder.

Front cover picture:
The original painting master of Captain Arthur Crown

The information in this book was compiled as accurately as possible at the time of going to
print. Please note that prices, names and other factual information, especially relating to
new products, is subject to change.

ISBN 0 9522155 3 5

Produced by Creativehouse, Aldershot.

Introduction

Colour Box miniatures were created in 1983 out of necessity. For ten years Peter Fagan had been running a modest craft company — Bronze Age Limited — based in the quiet Scottish Border town of Lauder, where he employed a handful of local people. He sculpted, cast and sold a range of cold cast bronzes (animal figurines, lamp stands etc.).

But by the early 1980s the future for bronzes was not looking rosy and Peter realised that a change in direction was required. So one day he took a bronze miniature of a cat and painted it, thus adding both colour and humour. The response from his customers was extraordinary — the new style sold like hotcakes. In a short space of time production of bronzes was replaced by hand painted ceramic resin miniatures and Peter had found his new direction.

It was something of a rebirth. From that point onwards Bronze Age Limited, using a new trading name of 'Colour Box' to reflect the new colourful image, started to grow. From a parochial craft company it gradually metamorphosed into a major giftware and collectable company, with a small army of employees producing tens of thousands of miniatures every week to satisfy a worldwide demand for sculptures by Peter Fagan.

So what happened? Where lies the secret of this sudden success? *Colour* was the key that unlocked the Colour Box, certainly, but it also unleashed qualities within Peter's work which had not been fully realised before — a nostalgia for childhood days, an impish sense of humour. These ingredients, combined with the ever popular subject of animals (cats in particular) made Home Sweet Home and Hopscotch two winning collections. Four years later the same appeal brought even greater success with the Teddy Bear Collection.

Peter understands collectors because he is a collector himself. His home is filled with all sorts of memorabilia and curios and the thought of an afternoon spent wandering in and out of antique shops attracts him greatly. This romantic attachment to things of the past he communicates through his models.

Affordability, too, has played an important role. Many of Peter Fagan's miniatures can be purchased at pocket money prices, which is more than can be said of most collectable ranges in the 1990s. No wonder the Colour Box Collectors Club has a high number of children amongst its members and that many children of a decade ago are today still eager collectors in their teens and early twenties.

Then there is the sheer appeal of Peter's work, the intangible, the image that creates an emotional response. His pieces make you smile, they remind you of your own childhood — not an idealistic memory, but how things really were, with milk bottles knocked over on the doorstep, clothes hanging from a drawer, furniture chipped and damaged, teddy bears hugged out of shape and with fur worn away.

Whatever the reasons, Peter Fagan's Colour Box miniatures are one of the most popular collectables around and Peter one of the most prolific artists. Since colour superseded bronze, he has sculpted over 700 figurines and around 30 million miniatures have left the Scottish Borders, every one hand cast and hand painted. The time has come for a catalogue of his work!

In two volumes — *A Collectors Guide to Colour Box Teddy Bears* and *A Collectors Guide to Colour Box Home Sweet Home and Other Collections* — I have attempted to list every miniature (current and retired) ever produced under the Colour Box name, plus details of manufacture, painting and mould variations, colourways, rare and unreleased items, Colour Box memorabilia and a secondary market price guide. In other words, everything you could possibly need to know about Colour Box. I may or may not have succeeded; it's difficult to tell with an artist as prolific as Peter Fagan as there may always be some forgotten piece lurking in a collection somewhere waiting to be catalogued.

The information contained herein has been compiled with the full cooperation of Bronze Age Limited and Frances and Peter Fagan in particular, the finer points being honed during two weeks of research in Lauder. Some of my time there was spent in jail . . . read on!

John Hughes
February 1995

About the Author

John Hughes was born in 1956 in Sutton Coldfield, West Midlands. He trained as a classical musician and gained an honours degree from London University in 1977. He then spent a number of years in music retailing, working for Harrods and Yamaha, during which time his first book — *Keyboard Magic* — was published by A & C Black. In 1985 he joined John Hine Limited, makers of David Winter Cottages, initially to develop a music recording branch of the company. But he very soon found himself side-stepping into the world of collectables and giftware and for the next eight years was involved in establishing and developing the David Winter Collectors Guild. In 1993 he left John Hine Limited and, together with Heather Lavender, established Collectables Publishing Limited (CPL) to produce books about collectable ranges. It was then that he became aware of the collectability of Colour Box and acquired his first piece — August String-Bear. In 1994 he and Heather approached Peter Fagan with a view to collaborating on a book about Colour Box. Such was Peter's enthusiasm for the project that six months later the two volumes were complete. John currently has seven published books to his credit (plus an unpublished novel!). He lives in Surrey with his wife, Chris, and daughters, Helen and Alice. In his spare time he enjoys listening to, and occasionally composing, music.

Contents

The Colour Box Story

The Colour Box story is primarily the story of one man, sculptor Peter Fagan. He was born on 5th November 1942. His father was from Galway on the West Coast of Ireland and his mother's family stems from Scotland, but despite these deeply Celtic roots Peter was actually born and bred in Essex. It was there, on the lower edge of East Anglia, that he spent his formative years and where many of the people, places and things existed that were to inspire Home Sweet Home, the first Colour Box collection, some thirty years later.

Peter was the artist of the family (he is the eldest of five children) and his ability was apparent at a very early age. His first school report, when he was five, said that he was *"excellent in plasticine and should do well with his modelling."* — prophetic words, and to this day Peter still uses plasticine to create his original figurines.

On graduating from Colchester College of Art in the early 1960s, Peter tried his hand at a number of jobs, beginning with a stint as a bus conductor (*"an excellent cure for shyness,"* he says!). Then he taught pottery at Braintree College of Further Education and worked as an assistant in an art studio where, amongst other prestigious commissions, he was responsible for casting the avante-garde bronze sculptures in Coventry Cathedral. At that time he also produced a great many relief panels.

One day he saw a vacancy advertised for an exhibition stand designer with a large company. Despite lacking any experience, Peter applied and managed to talk himself into the job. For a number of years he worked on exhibitions both in the UK and abroad, and when he left the company, he fulfilled several large commissions for theatres, prestige offices and a church.

At this point in his career Peter felt the need for a completely fresh start. So in 1972, with no specific plans in mind, he sold his house and drove up to Scotland where he had once spent an enjoyable holiday. After several weeks touring around, and looking at properties in the Highlands, he eventually moved back further south to the Borders. *"I ran out of petrol in Lauder,"* he says, *"and there I stayed."*

That was on a Friday. At 7.30am the next morning he awoke to the sound of a brass band, horses' hooves and whisky toasts in the street outside! He had arrived just in time to witness the Lauder Common Riding, an ancient traditional ceremony in which local people ride around the boundaries of the town to ensure that adjoining landowners have not encroached upon the "Common Lands of the Burgh."

To pay the bills, Peter got a job in a local factory and began taking private commissions, primarily making relief plaques — clan crests, coats of arms — and even pub signs. Living in a house on the High Street, he had some of his plaques on display in The Eagle Hotel a few yards down the road, and well remembers on occasions taking orders in the bar then rushing home to make the plaques! Some of his work from this period can still be seen in and around Lauder. Most notable are four coats of arms in Lauder church, sculpted to celebrate its tercentenary in November 1973.

Earlier the same year Peter had wandered into a craft shop and seen some figurines of

Before Colour Box there was Bronze Age. Left: A selection of Peter Fagan's animal figurines in cold cast bronze. Far left: Peter at work in his Lauder studio in the 1970s.

owls made in cold cast bronze resin. He thought to himself, *"I can do that,"* and promptly went home and set to work. In a short time he had modelled, cast and polished a selection of animal figurines and was soon doing the rounds of local shops with a bag full of pieces. *"If the shopkeepers didn't like them,"* he recalls, *" I'd pretend I hadn't made them and even offer to take back their critical comments to the artist, promising better next time!"* But enough shopkeepers did like them for a business to materialise and in 1973 Bronze Age Limited was established.

Production took place initially in and around Peter's house in Lauder — 11 West High Street — with people working in different rooms. His first employee was Myra Whellans. *"I worked in the little bedroom at Granny Baxter's,"* she remembers (Granny Baxter owned the house before Peter). Business gradually developed and by 1975 the company employed ten people. *"Peter was sculpting in another bedroom,"* Myra says, *"there were polishers in the kitchen and casting was done in the loft of the old stable belonging to the grocer. Then eventually I moved into the jail!"*

Lauder jail consists of three cells under the Town Hall; two with small grated windows and one (called the 'Black Hole') without any window at all. Its use as a jail was discontinued in 1843, and when Peter Fagan first rented it in the 1970s he used one cell as a shop, the other (where Myra worked) as a packing room and the Black Hole for storage. Myra remembers an American arriving one day and asking for Peter. She directed him to 'Granny Baxter's' in the High Street; and thus Bronze Age received their first

order for the USA!

The next move was to one of three workshop units on the town's Orchard Estate (known as 'top factory') and in time the company has expanded into all three. By the end of the 1970s the product range had also expanded: animal figurines varying from large prestige pieces such as a Welsh Cob to a collection of tiny ones called 'Tiddlers'; there were also plaques, lamp stands and paperweights.

By the early 1980s, however, it was clear to Peter Fagan that interest in bronze figurines was waning. He also felt that artistically he had done all he could within the medium. So in late 1982, as an experiment, he took a small bronze figurine of a cat and painted it. *"The response was extraordinary,"* he says. *"It sold like wildfire."* Soon the Hopscotch range of miniature painted animals appeared and within a few months they were generating a quarter of Bronze Age Limited's turnover. Other bronze sculptures were adapted to create the Miniature Collection.

Clearly this was the way of the future and Peter proceeded to re-think the entire product range. He changed from using cold cast resin to a ceramic resin and employed hand painters to create warm, natural colours on the pieces. Then he worked on the idea of placing the highly popular cat models into different situations, combining humour with nostalgia. His first notion was of a cat foraging in a dustbin for food, and this became Trash Can Cat, the very first Home Sweet Home piece to be sculpted.

Calling upon his past and happy boyhood memories, Peter gradually developed a collection. In those days he had a primitive but effective means of market research; sculptures in the front window of his house in Lauder High Street and see what people's reactions were. Passers-by were soon knocking on the door and asking about the funny cat models, and this positive sign was cemented by the hundreds of orders from shops that came flooding in after the first showing of the pieces at the Spring Trade Fair in early 1983. Home Sweet Home was a great success from the start. Bronze sculptures were abandoned.

It was in 1983 that Peter also devised a name to reflect the move towards more colourful models. He chose 'Colour Box' to suggest his own old paint box and the fact that each piece is hand painted. 'Colour Box' is a trading name, but to this day Peter has never changed the company name which still remains Bronze Age Limited. However, in the same year an American distributor was appointed and for the USA the name 'Adorables' was chosen instead of 'Colour Box.'

During the mid 1980s Home Sweet Home went from strength to strength whilst other collections fell by the wayside and were retired (Baby Animals, The Mutts). Then in 1987 Peter was on holiday in Belgium with his wife Frances. One wet afternoon in Bruges they took shelter in an old curios shop and there amongst the bric-a-brac he spied a number of old teddy bears — four in all. He purchased three of them (soon to be christened Robert, Peregrine and August String Bear) and after a sleepless night of regret at leaving the fourth, went back the next day for Gustav von Bruin. With the names came imaginary histories which the Fagans devised together and Frances wrote down, and in Peter's mind the idea for a new collection began to formulate.

The Teddy Bear Collection was launched the following year (1988), and Peter found himself with a success on his hands to rival that of Home Sweet Home. As a setting for the bears he sculpted a model of the curios shop in Bruges where the idea had originated and on a return visit discovered yet another bear for the collection — Johann. More real bears were acquired, mainly from auction rooms, and as the Fagans' own collection developed so too did the range of sculptures (40 pieces in the first three years), often with a familiar bear placed in an amusing or nostalgic setting. That every

new bear in the range is a sculpture of a real bear owned by Peter and Frances has remained a unifying factor throughout. It has also been Peter's inspiration. He says: *"The attraction to me of the real bears is that they belonged to someone and are therefore part of them, and that's what I try to capture."*

The arrival of teddy bears coincided with the launch of the Colour Box Collectors Club in June 1987. This was well received by collectors for two reasons: first because a regular Club newsletter provided them with much needed news and information about their collections; secondly, Peter Fagan started sculpting special pieces available exclusively for Club members. Within three years there were 10,000 members and by the end of 1994 Colour Box had recruited more than 40,000 in seven years.

Frances Fagan had been helping with the Collectors Club newsletter from the beginning by writing articles and answering letters. In 1989 she became full time editor and has been the driving force behind the Club ever since. She has also skillfully created storylines for the bears that she and Peter have adopted and named (if their history isn't already known).

On July 8 1989 the Colour Box shop and visitors centre was opened in the Old Smiddy, the oldest building in Lauder and, coincidentally, almost opposite the jail where Myra Whellans used to work (and which to this day still houses the Colour Box archives). The shop has always been run by Pat Learmonth who has welcomed a continuous stream of visitors ever since.

In the 1990s the popularity of the Teddy Bear Collection has increased considerably, and so has the collection. One of the prime sources for new bears has been Christie's in London and the Fagans have become familiar faces in the famous auction rooms whenever teddies are featured in the catalogue. When Christie's first ever sale devoted entirely to teddy bears was held on 6th December 1993, Peter and Frances reciprocated by donating 40 lots, the proceeds of which went to charity (Child Accident Prevention Trust). The lots included the masters of some of Peter's sculptures, real plush covered teddy bears and all ten of a limited edition piece sculpted specially for the occasion — The Auction Room. This event more than anything established Colour Box as highly collectable, if there was ever any doubt!

As well as the main collections, Colour Box have, in recent years, established a portfolio of additional prestigious work — the Edward Harrod, Lawleys, Hermann and Steiff collections, plus pieces for British Airways, Barclaycard Profiles and other commissions. As well as the Christie's sale, the Fagans have also regularly generated projects to raise money for selected charities, usually involving the donation of profits from the sale of pieces (e.g. Cat Napper, Teddy Randell, Safety Ted, Teddy Royale).

Peter Fagan has always been one for trying new ventures and with Home Sweet Home and Teddy Bears as the two main ranges, he has produced a number of projects which have met with varying degrees of success: Tableaux, Celebration Cakes, Menus, Early Days, Town and Country Collection. In the case of the last two, he encountered the problem of promoting sculptures which were 'Colour Box' but not 'Peter Fagan' and in the eyes of ardent collectors the two were (and still are) synonymous. To bypass this problem, in 1990 he established Cavalcade, a sister company to run parallel with Colour Box and to promote the work of other artists. Collections marketed undr the Cavalcade name are as follows: , Bear Facts, Beasties of the Kingdom, The Bogeymen, British Blighters, Bugs Bunny and Friends, The Cheddars, The Class, Dragon Keep, Eggbert and Friends, Fairweather, The Herd, In the Doghouse, Mr Stubbs, Secrets of the Forest, Perrfect Pets, Whiskers Cats and Dogs, and the World of Krystonia.

1993 saw the launch of a number of new Colour Box collections — Pennywhistle Lane, Good Golly, Arthur the Cat. Of specific interest is Pennywhistle Lane as it represents an entirely new concept for a collection; not just cats or bears but a selection of characters and items (including a whole family of mice) that inhabit the loft of a house.

In the USA Pennywhistle Lane is currently used as an umbrella title for a collection of pieces selected from all the Colour Box ranges being distributed by the Enesco Corporation, and replaces the 'Adorables' range. However, Teddies are also available as a separate collection under the name 'Centimental Bears'. Home Sweet Home cats are due to be launched under their own range name in 1996.

The connection with Enesco is one of a number of projects which will lead Peter Fagan and Bronze Age Limited into exciting new directions during the second half of the 1990s. The other important change is the amalgamation in 1995 of Colour Box and Cavalcade under one name Colour Box — The World of Peter Fagan. Thus Peter's work and that of other artists will all be identified as the product of Colour Box studios, including The Herd and Eggbert and Friends from the Cavalcade collections plus new collections — Lakeland Bears and Little Darlings.

Colour Box is a delightful success story. It started with a few sculptures sold from a bag and is currently a multi-million marketing concern. In twelve years Peter Fagan has created over 700 miniatures and his work can be bought in as many as 35 countries worldwide.

And the Colour Box story continues . . .

Collecting Colour Box

HOW COLOUR BOX FIGURINES ARE MADE

SCULPTING When sculpting Peter Fagan works from home in an attic studio overlooking the beautiful Tweed river. His raw material is plasticine and an original model he creates is always the same size as the final painted piece which a collector buys. To achieve the fine detail on his work he uses an array of small modelling tools, plus anything suitable for the purpose, including dental equipment, hat pins and embroidery utensils. He once scoured every junk shop in the Borders for a tea strainer fine enough to create the texture of the poodle wool on the Frou Frou's (Personality Pups).

"I find it hard to get started sometimes," he admits, *"but I'm alright once I get going. I listen to the radio as I work — Radio 4 usually. Some pieces come quicker than others and, surprisingly, it's often the quicker ones that tend to work better as far as I am concerned and also be more popular with collectors. Cats are more difficult to sculpt than teddy bears because although we own three cats of our own, I'm not sculpting an exact model every time. Having done so many models now I need to use source material more than I used to — books, periodicals. I'm also more precise these days. For example, if I'm sculpting a drawer I will construct it like a carpenter would, assembling each piece with dovetail joints. Then if it needs to look like an old drawer I'll 'distress' it. I didn't take so much care with the earlier models and now I'm embarrassed when I look at them!*

"Sculpturally I 'build' rather than 'cut away'. In other words I don't start with a large block and chisel away at it; I prefer to assemble pieces bit by bit, as with the drawer. This applies to large or small pieces, and in fact large pieces are an assembly of lots of small pieces, if you think about it."

When a model is finished, it is kept cold in a freezer so the plasticine is not easily damaged or distorted, and then taken to the mould makers at the 'top factory' in Lauder.

MOULD MAKING To create a master mould Peter's plasticine original is first surrounded by four walls of cardboard. Liquid silicon rubber is then poured over it until the plasticine is fully submerged. When the rubber has set the plasticine is removed from the space it has left inside the rubber block leaving a perfect mould of Peter's original (which is destroyed in the process). From this block mould a number of 'copies' of Peter's original are cast in tough, durable green resin ('greenware'). The quantity depends on the size of the piece: a large piece may have less than ten production masters, whereas smaller pieces have thirty or more. The masters can be used to make more moulds of the same piece, and by doing so Peter's original can be duplicated in large numbers. (These masters are themselves highly collectable, though only released by Colour Box under exceptional circumstances. A collection of sixty-three original working masters, representing all the original bears purchased at Christie's South Kensington by Frances and Peter Fagan between 1989 and 1993 were sold at the Christie's auction in 1993 and fetched £605!)

CASTING, GRINDING AND FETTLING In the casting shop, the moulds are filled with a liquid mixture of ceramic and resin which, with the aid of a slow trip through an oven, sets hard in under two hours. Still warm, the pieces are carefully removed from the moulds and taken in trays to have the bases trimmed flat. This is done using high speed circular grinders. The 'whiteware' (as unpainted pieces are called) is then 'fettled' — flashes of excess ceramic which sometimes occur during casting are removed using dental burrs. After fettling the pieces are wash-sprayed in a liquid not unlike nail varnish and then dried in preparation for painting.

PAINTING Colour Box miniatures are painted primarily by outworkers who collect whiteware from a number of 'stations' dotted around the Borders region, paint the pieces

Safety Ted being extracted from a block mould in the casting shop at Lauder. Moulds are made of durable silicon rubber and can be used many times over. The pieces themselves are cast in a mixture of ceramic and resin.

at home and return them when complete. There are also two workshops (at Haddington and Berwick upon Tweed) where painting is done 'in-house'. Before being let loose, however, they must undergo intensive training from skilled Colour Box tutors on a one-to-one basis, and even then it may take up to three years before they can tackle the more difficult sculptures. Painting time varies enormously: Paisley or Peregrine may take just a few minutes, but something like The Curios Shop can keep even the most experienced Colour Box painter occupied for up to six hours.

At one time the colours for a new piece were originated by Peter himself, but for a number of years this has been the task of Terry Fairbairn. She has more than 250 standard colours to choose from and can spend several days working on one piece. When they first started working together Peter used to brief her about the colours he had in mind, but nowadays there is no need as they are so much on the same wavelength that Terry invariably gets it right first time.

PACKING AND DESPATCH   Painted pieces are then finished by adding velour (larger pieces only) and a label and then wrapping and boxing them ready for despatch to shops all over the UK and the world.

VARIATIONS AND COLOURWAYS

Occasionally a Colour Box miniature is altered after it has been released. This is done by modifying a 'master' and making new moulds. In this book these are called Mould Variations — the original is called 'Mould 1' and the modified version 'Mould

2'. When such a change is made, the original version (Mould 1) becomes retired and acquires a secondary market value, effectively as a 'limited edition' of unknown number — even if the Mould 2 version is still currently available. All known mould variations are itemised in Section Two as part of the information about individual pieces. However, there are very few indeed in the Teddy Bear Collection, though more common in other Colour Box ranges (notably Home Sweet Home).

Far more common, however, are variations to the colours of pieces. These exist for a number of reasons:

1) A conscious decision by Colour Box to change the colours during production.

2) Slight differences between the work of individual painters.

3) Deliberately modified versions of a piece (called 'colourways' or 'paintways') created in limited numbers for a special event or purpose, such as a store promotion or charity (e.g. Prudence, Buster).

Colour Box do not possess definitive records of mould or colour variations. However, all available information is listed in Section Two, and this has been enhanced by details of pieces in individual collections. But further variations are bound to exist.

CODE NUMBERS

Within certain collections (Home Sweet Home, Hopscotch) it may appear that the code numbers of some figurines have been duplicated. In fact Colour Box occasionally reallocate numbers from retired pieces to new ones (e.g. Festive Fun, Bright and Early -

Right: A selection of early pieces with the original Home Sweet Home boxes which Colour Box used until the late 1980s. Far right: From top to bottom, examples of an early, middle and late base label.

both HS319) and rarely are two figurines with the same number both current at the same time. Exceptions are: Home Sweet Home — Piano Pops and Washtand, both HS213 and current together between 1988 and 1992. One number — H16 in the Hopscotch collection — has been used three times (Snake, Lion, Mouse).

Generally speaking the first digit of a code number in the Home Sweet Home collection identifies the price band of the piece, and the higher the number the lower the value. This has not been adhered to strictly over the years and there are many exceptions. Also pieces such as Limited Editions do not apply.

Colour Box sculptures and memorabilia code numbers are prefixed by the following letters:

BK - Books, CA = Arthur (also used for Cards), CC = Collectors Club (since 1993), CM = Ceramics, DG = Personality Pups, GG = Good Golly, H = Hopscotch, HS = Home Sweet Home, MC = Miniature Collection, PL = Pennywhistle Lane, PS = Pictures, TC = Teddy Bears, XHS / XTC = Christmas Collection.

BOXES AND PACKAGING

Between 1983 and 1989 Colour Box miniatures were supplied in white boxes (assorted sizes) with brown illustrations of a cottage exterior: the top of the box was sloped like a roof and the front face was remov-able. The main text reads: 'Colour Box Miniatures.' In 1989 these were replaced by the red, green and blue boxes in various sizes which are still current in 1995 and at the same time the new 'Colour Box' logo was also created. Yellow boxes were also introduced for the Miniature Collection. Both the boxes and the logo were designed to reflect the 'Colour Box' name. Prior to the introduction of the new boxes, Teddies were issued in plain pink boxes with a Colour Box sticker attached. Inside all boxes the packaging has always consisted of either tissue paper or 'bubble-wrap'.

Prestige limited edition pieces (e.g. The Schoolroom) are presented in customised silk-lined boxes.

STORY LEAFLETS

Stories have always been an important part of the Teddy Bear Collection and every named bear is accompanied by his own story leaflet, written by Frances Fagan. This also applies to Pennywhistle Lane but not to the Hopscotch, Personality Pups or Miniature collections. The stories are sometimes true, sometimes imaginary, and sometimes a blend of the two. On several fictional storylines have turned out to be uncannily accurate or the subject of remarkable coincidences, much to Frances' astonishment (e.g. Martin, Binkie, Teddy Randell, Teddy Robinson). The stories behind the stories are the subject of a book in its own right!

LABELS AND VELOUR

LABELS The paper labels (sometimes called 'backstamps') to be found on the base of all but the tiniest pieces. They have varied slightly over the years and this can be useful in identifying the approximate production date of a piece. All Colour Box labels are blue and circular, but . . .

EARLY LABELS (1983 - 1986) state only: *Made and Hand Painted in Scotland.*

MIDDLE LABELS (1986 - 1992) state: *Made and Hand Painted in Scotland* plus Peter Fagan's signature and the year of issue.

RECENT LABELS (1993 onwards) state the name of the piece, a copyright symbol, the date of issue, the code number of the piece, but not the country of origin: e.g. *Upstairs Downstairs Peter Fagan © 1994 HS806.*

Consequently a piece such as The Academic or Lap of Luxury, sculpted in 1988 and retired in 1990, will only be found with an early or middle label, whilst Peter Bear or Teddy Robinson, issued in 1988 but still going strong in 1995, will be found with all three types of label.

Although the stickiness of labels fades with time and labels do fall off, every effort should be made to reattach them, as labels provide authenticity as well as factual information.

VELOUR Velour is attached to the base of larger miniatures but not smaller ones. By far the most common colour of the velour is red, although other colours are used from time to time. There is a very good practical reason for this: sometimes the village store in Lauder runs out of red velour!

In 1994 velour cut to the shape of a piece and covering the entire base was replaced by a number of small velour discs dotted across the base.

MARKINGS

The markings on Peter Fagan's sculptures vary considerably, from a simple touchmark (PF) to a complete signature, copyright symbol (©) and date — or any combination of these ingredients. Some pieces have no markings at all. During 1992 he used a stamp in the shape of a rosette to emboss the words HAND PAINTED and his signature, but the text was difficult to read and its use was discontinued. The rosette can be seen on some but not all 1992 releases (e.g. Klim, Benji, Prudence, Grand Prix Ted, Miranda, Jerome). Location of the markings also varies but they are always to be found on the visible faces, never on the base.

THE SECONDARY MARKET

When Bronze Age Limited produce a piece, they supply quantities to their authorised stockists (shops) who then sell them to their customers. This is called the 'primary market'. When the company chooses to discontinue (or 'retire') production of a piece, and once existing stocks have been sold, the piece will no longer be available from their stockists. The only way then to acquire the piece is either from another collector or

Left: An example of the collectability of Colour Box: Home Movies, issued in 1989 for £9.50, retired in 1990 and currently valued at £35-45. Pieces available for such a short period will be of particular interest on the secondary market.

Right: The Schoolroom, one of few Colour Box pieces issued in a pre-announced, numbered limited edition. Only 1,500 will ever be made.

from a dealer who specialises in the buying and selling of retired pieces. This is called the 'secondary market'.

When a regular figurine is retired it in effect becomes a 'limited edition', by virtue of the fact that it is no longer produced; this applies even though the edition size remains unknown. As a result, demand for the piece (and therefore its monetary value) increases. Ironically the most common reason for retiring a piece is that it has lost its appeal and is not selling well; but once it is retired, the opposite invariably applies.

The rate at which a piece increases in value depends upon its rarity value; the longer the production run the smaller the demand. For example, Fishermans Friend and Home Movies were only produced for three years (1988-90), whereas Peregrine and Humphrey, recently retired after eight years in production (1988-95).

Colourways produced for a special promotion or event are collectable as the number produced are usually quite limited. Serious collectors will often want to acquire every colourway version of the same piece and therefore pay premium prices on the secondary market.

Most collectable of all are the relatively few pieces produced in pre-announced, numbered limited editions (e.g. The Schoolroom [1,500]). Although more expensive initially, these are the figurines which will increase in value the most over a period of time. Similarly special commission bears for individual shops (e.g. Alfonzo, Little Archie, Johnson Bear) are invariably created

in limited editions.

Collectors for whom investment is a consideration should also be aware of the attraction of the Colour Box Collectors Club pieces. Not only is availability limited by time (usually one year) but also by number (total Club membership), and in the case of Club offers the percentage of Club members who choose to purchase the piece. These restrictions give them a collectability second only to numbered limited editions.

PLEASE NOTE It is important to point out that the buying and selling of retired pieces is carried out independently of Bronze Age Limited who, as the manufacturers, rightly maintain a policy of non-involvement in the secondary market.

COUNTERFEITS

When something is collectable it also, sadly, becomes the target of counterfeiters and in this respect Colour Box miniatures are on occasions no exception. Bronze Age Limited have traced replicas of their products to a number of countries including Spain, Greece, Sweden, France as well as the UK and Peter Fagan is very quick to respond in protecting his copyright, as the guilty parties have discovered to their cost! Peter has also been active in establishing the Giftware Copyright Protection Association.

From the collector's point of view there is nothing to be concerned about when buying a new labelled figurine in its box from an authorised Colour Box stockist. However, shops or individuals selling new unlabelled, unboxed pieces should be avoided and details passed onto Bronze Age Limited immediately.

Older pieces being sold on the secondary market are a different matter. People do not always keep boxes and, as mentioned earlier, labels can fall off. So when thinking of buying a piece from someone here are a few suggestions to bear in mind:

1) Always ask for the original box, packaging and leaflets.

1) Look closely for any loss of detail. Compare the piece with pictures in brochures, the Collectors Club magazines and this book.

2) Be aware of the quality of painting. Colour Box painters are thoroughly trained and quality control is high.

3) Ask questions about the piece's history. (Where did you get it from? How long have you had it?)

On the other hand, don't be over cautious! Counterfeiting is difficult, dangerous and, despite the information in this section, extremely rare.

SIGNED PIECES

Peter Fagan enjoys meeting and talking with collectors — he is after all a collector himself. He therefore regularly attends in-store promotions and special events where he signs his work. This signature is a precious addition to a piece and increases its inherent value; by how much monetarily is a very difficult question to answer, but it should be regarded as a significant advantage during resale and the vendor should be looking for a premium price. A signature should also be regarded as an indelible guarantee of authenticity.

WHERE SHOULD I BUY AND HOW MUCH SHOULD I PAY?

PRIMARY MARKET Colour Box figurines are available from Bronze Age Limited's extensive network of authorised stockists. The actual price of the pieces may vary slightly from shop to shop as stockists are not obliged to adhere to Recommended Retail Prices (indeed the company only started issuing R.R.P. lists for the first time in 1992). There are merits for shopping around, just as there are merits for establishing a good relationship with a shop which provides friendly, reliable and above all knowledgeable service.

SECONDARY MARKET There are a number of specialist dealers in retired collectables, most of whom are aware of the continuing popularity of both current and retired Colour Box figurines. For collectors wishing to purchase retired pieces they provide an excellent service. Most dealers advertise regularly in appropriate magazines and periodicals, some of which are listed in Section Three. Also, retired pieces can still be tracked down in shops at the original selling price, with a bit of time and effort.

Collectors selling pieces should bear in mind that a dealer will offer a price lower than the market value — 40% lower on average — but this fluctuates depending on circumstances, the number of pieces being sold at one time, their condition, and demand for particular pieces at the time. The importance of dealers to collectors, however, is that they have good stocks and excellent contacts with other buyers and sellers.

For collectors to acquire the full market value for their pieces, it is necessary to sell or exchange directly with other collectors. Making contact here is the problem. The classified sections of the magazines listed in Section Three is a possibility; however, word of mouth and developing contacts with other serious collectors is more desirable.

TAKING CARE OF YOUR COLLECTION

Although the ceramic/resin mix from which Colour Box miniatures are cast makes them very durable, they should nevertheless be treated with tender loving care to avoid chips and perhaps more serious damage. Should the worst happen, however, it is not necessarily the end of the world and the Colour Box Collectors Club organise a 'hospital' service. Please contact them for further information — Tel: (01578) 722780.

To dust your collection use a soft paint brush, toothbrush, make-up brush or a photographer's lens brush. For a more thorough clean, Colour Box figurines can be held briefly under a tap without affecting the paint. *BUT do not soak them in water for any length of time.*

Section Two

Introduction to Listings

All the sculptures in the collections are listed in order of code number irrespective of whether they are currently available or retired. Pieces in the Home Sweet Home collection which were never allocated code numbers can be found at the end of the list.

ISSUE AND RETIREMENT DATES

An 'Issue Date' is the year in which a particular piece was first made available for purchase by Colour Box; the season or month is also listed when known. This occasionally varies from the date marked on a figurine as Peter Fagan may have sculpted the piece in advance of its release.

A 'Retirement Date' is the year in which production of a piece ceases and it is withdrawn from the catalogue. In recent years 'retirements' have been announced in advance so that collectors have the opportunity to acquire a piece. But in the past retirements just happened if the popularity of a piece had waned.

It should be remembered that when a piece is retired it does not automatically disappear from shops. Stockists will continue to sell the piece for as long as stocks last. With a bit of detective work it is possible to track down stores who still have a piece on display at list price some considerable time after its retirement date.

ISSUE PRICES

'Issue Price' means the price for which pieces sold in shops when they were first released. This is useful information to compare with both the valuations of retired miniatures and also the most recent retail prices of current pieces.

All issue prices are intended as a guide only as individual shops are entitled to select their own selling prices. (For example, a Hopscotch piece selling in one store for £1.15 might be 99p elsewhere.) Prices between 1983 and 1991 have been reconstructed from known Colour Box trade prices and in most cases have been rounded to the nearest pound or 50p. From 1992 onwards Colour Box's Recommended Retail Price lists have been used. (The company did not issue R.R.P.s before then.)

TEXT

The text in italics narrates the inspiration and stories behind individual pieces and has been gleaned either from the story leaflets which accompany the pieces or from the Collectors Club magazine. This is primarily the work of Frances Fagan and is reproduced with her kind permission. The remaining text is factual information relating to the pieces themselves such as production variations, colourways etc.

PAINTING VARIATIONS

All Colour Box miniatures are handpainted and therefore vary slightly in colouration. It would be impossible to list every difference and the painting variations recorded in this book are primarily the known changes made by Colour Box during production. Special colourways for promotions and other events are also listed (in Section Three).

Teddy Bears Collection

Code: TC001
Issued: 1988
Issue Price: £65

TEDDY TALES

Code: HSP01
Issued: 1994
Issue Price: £29.50

THE CURIOS SHOP

*I*nto this cramped little shop in Bruges, Peter Fagan stepped out of the rain and discovered four teddy bears which were the genesis of the Teddy Bear Collection — Robert, Peregrine, August String Bear and Gustav von Bruin. Peter takes delight in any discarded treasures and seeing the four bears he wanted to give them all a new home. In no time they were bundled into bags and tucked under his arm, ready to start their journey with him into further exciting adventures.

BEA BEAR'S BARROW

*B*ea Bear is the fastest, sharpest, wheeler-dealer, second-hand junk barrow bear ever to be seen in the western world. Every day he went out on the old horse and cart with his master, collecting junk, old bedsteads, leftover stove pipes and lead piping and took it back to the yard for scrap. He came to Peter Fagan in bits from an auction in Edinburgh and required major surgery in the skilled hands of Dr Brian, the Colour Box teddy doctor. He then acquired a suitable outfit to match his trade and Frances Fagan christened him Bea Bear after her grandmother's old teddy which, sadly, was cuddled to bits back in the 1950s.

During production, the bear figurine is cast separately and then attached to the piece later. To cast the piece as a whole in a single mould would be impossible.

Code: TC002
Issued: Mar 1994
Issue Price: £29.75

GETTING BETTER

Code: TC003
Issued: Feb 1995
Issue Price: £24.95

THE FLOWER CART
Limited Edition

Code: TC004
Issued: Feb 1995
Edition Size: 1,500
Issue Price: £75

Code: TC011
Issued: Mar 1994
Issue Price: £18.75

MR GROWLER'S FIRST LESSON

*Y*ou might be forgiven if you thought that Mr Growler had got his name because he was bad tempered. In fact that was far from the truth as Mr Growler was a very happy man really and good fun when he was at work in the classroom. His name came from the fact that every time he tipped forward he made a deep sounding growl and his pupils at school nicknamed him "Mr Growler."

19

LONDON BEARS

The three pieces known as the London Bears joined the regular Colour Box range in February 1995. However, 100 signed copies were sold in Selfridges in August 1994 and a further quantity were sold at a promotion held by Raffles in Windsor in September 1994.

WARDER WINDSOR

Code: TC012
Issued: Aug 1994 (pre-release)
February 1995 (general release)
Issue Price: £18.75

PC HERO

Code: TC013
Issued: Aug 1994
Issue Price: £18.75

Code: TC014
Issued: Aug 1994 (prelease)
February 1995 (general release)
Issue Price: £18.75

SGT. PEPPERMINT

The pre-release version had a plume on his hat and just two stripes on his right sleeve (Mould 1). The plume was removed and a third stripe added prior to general release (Mould 2).

Teddy Bears Collection

LITTLE LONDON TRIPLETS

These three bears were available exclusively from Selfridges in London during 1994 and joined the regular Colour Box collection on 1st January 1995. They can be purchased individually or as a set with a box sleeve.

BEEFEATER

Code: TCL02
Issued: Aug 1994
Issue Price: £5.50

POLICEMAN

Code: TCL03
Issued: Aug 1994
Issue Price: £5.50

GUARDSMAN

Code: TCL04
Issued: Aug 1994
Issue Price: £5.50

● ● ● ● ● ● ● ● ● ● ● ● ● ● ● ● ● ● ● ●

Code: TC015
Issued: Feb 1995
Issue Price: £18.75

JONESY

Back in the war years, everyone had to be ready to defend their home territory against aggressors and many local volunteers were called in to the first line of defence. The Home Guard, as they were affectionately known, took to their duties with gusto and despite a distinct lack of funds and weapons they were ready to stand against the onslaught. Jonesy is ready for duty and with his tin hat and gas mask he helps to defend his country and keep safe the homes of his friends.

CHIMBLEY SWEEP

Code: TC016
Issued: July 1995
Issue Price: £18.75
No picture available prior to publication

There aren't many chimney sweeps left in old London town nowadays. All the laws were changed and smokey old fires are a thing of the past. But Chimbley Sweep the bear still finds work in the capital city and travels to the suburbs where he spends his life helping unblock and clean up all kinds of chimneys. His name came from one small boy who didn't manage to say 'chimney' quite right and Chimbley Sweep bear liked it so much he kept the name for himself. Chimney sweeps are known to be lucky and just one touch will bring you luck all day long!

ELIZA

Code: TC018
Issued: July 1995
Issue Price: £18.75
No picture available prior to publication

In the very early hours of the morning the market traders at Covent Garden used to prepare for the day. Long before dawn the stalls were set up and fruit and vegetables of all kind were sold. There were flower stalls, too, where the lovely blooms were displayed for the lords and ladies to decorate their homes. At the end of the day the market was often quite untidy with broken flower heads or bits of leafy decoration lying on the ground where the flower stands had been. Eliza could always be found picking up the blooms and leaves and tying them into pretty button holes and posies. Then she'd sit on the steps and sell her wares, for just a few pennies, from her old basket. She loved her life and her work and especially enjoyed Saturday nights when the crowds from the theatres made her best customers as the gentlemen always wore flowers in their button holes.

THE GUV

Code: TC017
Issued: July 1995
Issue Price: £18.75
No picture available prior to publication

"He's the boss," everyone said when they met the Guv. It wasn't just that he was the Cockney Pearly King, it was mainly because he took command of any situation, wherever he was! Pearly Kings and Queens wear beautiful costumes covered all over in real pearl buttons. They are considered the best in the East End of London where the tradition started and they parade in the streets on special occasions to show off their lovely clothes. It's anyone's guess how many buttons it took to make the Guv's costume. He says he knows exactly how many, but it's a real job to count them! Wish him luck if you meet him and he'll be sure to do the same for you!

BEAR BACK RIDER

Dougie bear has never ridden a real horse, but he has often thought about it. He decided to begin his riding lessons on the nursery play horse. All the other toys in the nursery thought he was being particularly brave, since he was only a small bear and they were worried that Dougie might have an accident and be thrown off. However, he persevered and is still determined to ride a real horse one day!

Code: TC019
Issued: Feb 1995
Issue Price: £18.75

TOYBOX

Code: TC110
Issued: 1988
Retired: 1992
Issue Price: £13

*S*itting with the old-fashioned toys, Gustav von Bruin reflects on his past when he lived with an orchestra and travelled the world. He can still remember much of the music which will always be a great comfort to him.

FISHERMANS FRIEND

Code: TC111
Issued: 1989
Retired: 1990
Issue Price: £14

*T*he friends in question are Jonathan and Christopher. Note the wealth of detail characteristic of all Peter's work: the fisherman's net, his pipe and knife lying on the bollard, the floats, fishing line and even a piece of seaweed washed up on the harbour step. Fishermans Friend has no signature or date.

WRITING HOME

Code: TC112
Issued: 1990
Retired: 1994
Issue Price: £12

*T*heodore has spent most of his life abroad or travelling around Europe and has always been a good correspondent. Letter writing has played a very important part of his life and he enjoys receiving letters as much as he enjoys writing them. The old writing case belonged in Peter's family and when Theodore set up residence with Peter he took it over.

During production of this piece, Theodore and the vase were cast separately. The original working master was auctioned at Christie's in 1993, in a lot which also included a painting of Theodore by Deidre Mackay Clark, the original working master of Theodore's Pastimes and a miniature of Theodore painted by a Colour Box master painter. The lot fetched £132.

BATHING BEACH

Happy memories of the long summer days digging on the sand. Summer holidays seemed hotter, ice creams cooler and sand was deeper to dig when we were all younger. This happy holiday piece featuring the bears is truly a delightful memory of those long hot lazy days of summer. Prior to release, Bathing Beach had the working title "In the Swim". During production the bear (Christopher) and the seagull were cast separately.

Code: TC113
Issued: 1990
Retired: 1993
Issue Price: £12

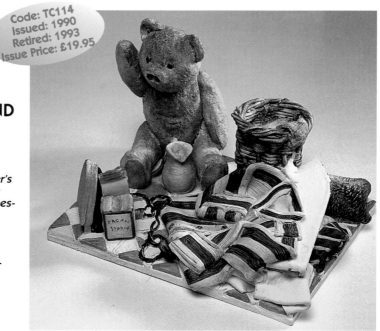

Code: TC114
Issued: 1990
Retired: 1993
Issue Price: £19.95

STARCH AND PRESS

Humphrey about to attack Peter's best shirt with the iron! In less domestic circumstances Humphrey is also Safety Ted!
The bear on this piece is cast separately.

FIRST AID POST

The bear featured on this piece, Roger, was cast separately. There are four paint variations to the cross on this piece. In the autumn of 1991 the International Red Cross contacted Colour Box to inform them that the use of the red cross on First Aid Post was in breach of the Geneva Convention! So Colour Box decided to change the cross to green. However, pieces in shops with the red cross (Version 1) were left unchanged, and pieces in production which had already been given a red cross were overpainted with a matt green paint (it proved impossible to remove the red paint). This gave the effect of a deep green cross with feint red edges (Version 2). New, unpainted pieces, were originally given several coats of green to create a gloss effect (Version 3), but by the end of 1992 just one coat had become standard to give a matt green effect (Version 4). Of these four versions, the first two are rare.

Pieces already in production which had received their red crosses were painted over in green. The same changes were made to Kiss It Better in the Home Sweet Home Collection and Tender Care from the Early Days Range.

STORYTIME

The bears on the chair are Peregrine and August String-Bear. Both are cast separately during production and then glued into place.

BIRTHDAY SURPRISES

Originally issued as Christmas Surprises (XTC118) and then repainted without Christmas colouring (but not remodelled in any way) to become Birthday Surprises. All trimmings were later removed by remodelling the 'greenware' master mould to reveal . . . Bartholomew (TC226)!

CAPTAIN ARTHUR CROWN

Code: TC119
Issued: Sept 1991
Issue Price: £12.50

Peter and Frances bought a very old, faded blue teddy at a Christie's sale. The bear was in a poor condition (torn ear, only one eye, no nose or mouth and hardly any stuffing) and cost very little. Consequently, on the train ride home, he was christened Arthur Crown ('alf a crown). A few days later he received some much needed first aid (restuffing, new nose etc.) including a black patch to cover the missing eye, and Lucy, the Fagans' youngest daughter, dressed him in a captain's uniform and gave him his full title — Captain Arthur Crown!

GRANDMA ROSIE

Code: TC120
Issued: Jun 1992
Retired: Spring 1995
Issue Price: £12.99

*G*randma Rosie loves hats — hats of all shapes and sizes. But she was never satisfied and was after the ultimate hat, to wear at the races. She tried everywhere to find it but without success. Then Mrs Patterson, who lived next door, suggested that Grandma Rosie should make a hat, the best hat in the universe! Grandma Rosie set to work. She found last year's straw hat and went to call on all her friends and relations to borrow something from all of them: "I'm making the best hat in the universe!" she said. And so she did. Everyone gave her something for her hat and Grandma Rosie was delighted. "I shall be the talk of the races," she said proudly." And she was.

MARTIN

Code: TC121
Issued: Mar 1993
Issue Price: £12.99

A *ble Seaman Martin Bear was known to his*
friends as Martin the Mariner. A jolly, good-
natured, affable sailor always on the point of
raising anchor and setting off on one voyage or
another. He was most famous for his deep baritone
voice and the seemingly endless repertoire of sea
shanties that he sang as he went about his duties on
deck. He felt he had grown a little too old and portly
for the hornpipe, though; perhaps a tot or two too
much rum in his youth had put paid to that!
The real Martin bear was purchased by Frances and
Pete Fagan at a Hugglets Teddy Festival in London
and named after a collector who was present on the
same day. Frances then went away and created the
storyline for Martin without knowing anything more
about the man who had donated his name. By the
time of the next festival, Martin (the Colour Box
miniature) had been produced and Martin (the man)
confronted Frances, wanting to know how she had
found out so much about him — her story leaflet
had been uncannily accurate! It was no more than a
coincidence, but one of several similar examples in
which fiction has coincided with fact.

Code: TC122
Issued: Mar 1993
Issue Price: £12.99

THE HAPPY COUPLE

A *glimpse of romantic love as everyone dreams*
of it! Miepi and Barti Bear are joined together
in Holy Matrimony and couldn't be happier. A
more ideally matched couple could not be found any-
where and the exchange of teddy wedding rings and
that most sought after of kisses has sealed their union
forever.

Code: TC123
Issued: Sept 1993
Issue Price: £12.99

PERAMBULATION

Teddy Bears Collection

Code: TC124
Issued: Dec 1993
Issue Price: £12.99

LORD PAUL

Named after the Managing Director of Christie's, Paul Barthaud. Lord Paul was launched at Harrods on 3rd December 1993 and the first piece sold was a special piece mounted on a plinth signed by Peter Fagan, Peter Bolliger (Managing Director of Harrods) and Louise Pankhurst (Director of the Child Accident Prevention Trust). Anyone spending £25 or more on the day also received a Lord Paul commemorative tea towel. Lord Paul also appears on The Auction Room, the limited edition of 10 created for the 1993 Christie's teddy bear auction. All ten pieces were painted differently, but for general release, Lord Paul's painting style was standardised: just one colour was used for his body, his gavel became brown and his circular badge was left plain.

Code: TC210
Issued: 1988
Retired: 1992
Issue Price: £9.50

HOLIDAY BEAR

Robert sits optimistically on his holiday trunk. Once a sleek, golden mohair bear, he has faded a little but his cheerful face and endearing smile are ever present to encourage us all towards a better future.

Code: TC211
Issued: 1989
Retired: 1990
Issue Price: £9.50

HOME MOVIES

Featuring Dickie Bear (watching himself on screen, perhaps). Notice how the projector is resting on some well thumbed books to make sure the film is screened at the right height. What other films are to be found in the box . . . ? Dickie Bear was cast separately during production of this piece. The touchmark reads: '© PF 89.'

TRAIN-SPOTTER ▶

Peregrine lived much of his life in a very well-populated nursery in St. James's. This sculpture shows Peregrine at his happiest amongst other beautiful Sunday toys awaiting the chance to play. Peregrine was cast separately during production.

Code: TC212
Issued: 1990
Retired: 1993
Issue Price: £10

Code: TC213
Issued: 1990
Retired: 1993
Issue Price: £10

TUCKBOX

That's Dickie Bear indulging in one of his favourite pastimes — raiding the tuckbox for sweeties!

NIGHT AT THE OPERA

The theatre is Ralph's great love. He dreams of the days when he wore top hats, capes and white silk scarves. He remembers well the evenings spent in the box at the Opera, peering at the singers, and being ready to present flowers to the leading lady after the show.

BAKING DAY

Jilly Bear's favourite pastime is featured in this, her special miniature. Jilly loves to help with the baking, her green pinny protects her from the flour as she makes all sorts of lovely cakes and pastries.

Code: TC214
Issued: 1990
Retired: 1993
Issue Price: £10

Code: TC215
Issued: 1990
Retired: 1994
Issue Price: £10

Teddy Bears Collection

FLYING ACE

*A*ction in the heavens is what excites Sopwith most. He still feels a thrill when he hears the roar of an aeroplane engine. His memories of the Royal Flying Corps are still fresh in his mind and the magic of the old bi-planes will never fade for this special aviator bear.

Prior to release, Flying Ace had the working title "Flight Plan".

Code: TC216
Issued: 1990
Retired: 1993
Issue Price: £10

BUSTER

*O*riginally Buster's family came from Sweden. His first family stayed in a smart flat in Stockholm and he liked to watch the busy shopping street from the second floor window. He lived with a little boy and his younger sister who shared him for several years until his 'brother' Eric arrived. When the children felt they were "too big" for bears, Buster and Eric found themselves at a Bear Festival in Berlin, then a Collectors' Fair in London and finally Colour Box, where they are the "gentle giants" of the collection.

Code: TC217
Issued: Sept 1991
Retired: Spring 1995
Issue Price: £9.75

Several colourways of Buster have been produced: 1) with a blue top and 'B' on breast pocket as a corporate gift for Blue Chip Travel in Edinburgh, Christmas 1992; 2) with sage green top and 'N J B' on front in December 1993 for Not Just Bears in New Zealand; 3) with red and green top in October 1993 for Lawleys, Reading.

Code: TC218
Issued: Sept 1991
Issue Price: £9.75

OLLIE

*O*llie particularly enjoyed the cold weather (in fact he always wanted to be a polar bear!) and sports a wonderfully bright jacket and hat which have been made for him. He had first fallen in love with the winter weather when he went on holiday with his family to the ski resort of Aviemore in Scotland. The clean, crisp air and the smell of pine needles excited him immensely and when it actually began to snow he grew really very agitated to go out in it. Tobogganing was Ollie's favourite and he was often thrown off into the powdery whiteness amongst a roar of laughter and the clatter of the sledge. Ollie has been on several winter holidays since he came to live with Peter Fagan and is always excited if the weather forecast is bad!!

BENJI

Benji Bear had just one ambition in life. Above everything else he desperately wanted to ride in a hot air balloon. Eventually his dream was realised one day at a summer fair. When Benji and his family got to the fairground, there, in the middle was the biggest, reddest, hot air balloon that Benji had ever seen. It wasn't long before Benji was floating up above the fairground — and he has never looked back, always determined that one day he will do it again.

Code: TC220
Issued: Mar 1992
Retired: 1994
Issue Price: £9.99

PEMBERTON

Pemberton had rather wobbly limbs as a result of being misused by a group of children in the nursery school. He was rescued by Mrs Camberley, the dinner lady, who dressed him up in a smart blue suit that had belonged to her grandson, Christopher. Pemberton was then allowed back into the nursery class only if he was treated with greater respect by the children. Their teacher, Mrs Arnold, insisted that he sat on the large red beanbag at story time and helped her turn over the pages, and every week one child was chosen to be "Pemberton's special helper."

Code: TC221
Issued: Mar 1992
Retired: Spring 1995
Issue Price: £9.99

Code: TC222
Issued: Jun 1992
Issue Price: £9.99

GRAND PRIX TED

MIRANDA

Code: TC223
Issued: Jun 1992
Retired: 1994
Issue Price: £9.99

Miranda had lived all her life in a local sweet shop on the corner of a village green in Shropshire. The old lady who ran the shop had adopted Miranda some years previously whilst on a touring holiday of Western Europe. Miranda had been left on the coach and after many enquiries no-one had claimed her, so the old lady brought her back to the quiet little country village shop. There she sat on the counter near the till while the lady weighed humbugs and measured liquorice skipping ropes for all the local children. Miranda became quite famous before moving on to Oxford and eventually Colour Box.

BUMBLE

Bumble is a real honey bear! He loves honey and would do almost anything to have a sticky spoonful. He lived for many years with an old lady in Somerset. She kept bees and had three white-slatted wooden hives in a small apple orchard at the bottom of her garden. Every so often she would put on a lot of strange clothes, including an enormous hat with a mesh veil. Then off she went to open the hives and collect the honey, and Bumble would go with her. Bumble now lives with Peter Fagan and still loves honey sandwiches.

A Bumble colourway with red and white scarf was produced in October 1993 for Lincoln Co-op.

Code: TC224
Issued: Jun 1992
Retired: Spring 1995
Issue Price: £9.99

Code: TC225
Issued: Jun 1992
Retired: 1994
Issue Price: £9.99

JEROME

Jerome had been in chambers for many years before he finally came to rest in the offices of Wander, Tappitt and Trip, solicitors of some repute, near London's famous Lincolns Inn. A bear of legal brain and nimble wit, the counsel of Jerome was often sought by juniors and clerks. However, his greatest claim to fame was when he was allowed to attend a court case at the Old Bailey itself when Rodney Waxlaurel, QC, felt the need of Jerome's support in a case. Now Jerome offers sensible advice to younger bears in the Colour Box hug.

Teddy Bears Collection

BARTHOLOMEW

Code: TC226
Issued: Oct 1992
Retired: 1993
Issue Price: £9.99

Bartholomew was named after his favourite uncle, Great Uncle Bartholomew or "Bartie" for short. They shared a passion for vintage motor cars and Bartholomew regularly attended the London to Brighton Rallies, seated up high on the beautiful buttoned leather upholstery of his great uncle's Bentley. He loved the smells of the old vehicles, the petrol, the teak oil and polishes, but perhaps best of all, the peppermint humbugs that Great Uncle Bartie used to offer to all his travelling companions. In a previous life Bartholomew was known as Christmas Surprises (XTC118) and Birthday Surprises (TC118) with suitably celebratory trimmings.

SAFETY TED

Humphrey shows that he's sensible when he's on his bike or his skateboard. He's well kitted out so as to prevent serious injury if he did have an accident. He says that he wants all young teddy collectors to know that accidents are the biggest killer of children in the UK and he wants all youngsters and grown-ups to do their best to prevent them.

A competition was held in the Collectors Club Newsletter to design a bear to help raise money for the Child Accident Prevention Trust, and Safety Ted (a.k.a. Humphrey) is based on the winning design submitted by Jane Lane of Sutton Valence. Net profits of this special bear throughout the first year of the launch were donated to CAPT — a total in excess of £23,000.

JACK

Jack the bear had one driving ambition — he longed to catch up with Captain Arthur Crown, that affable rogue who has sailed the seven seas in pursuit of piracy and damsels. Jack wanted to give him a taste of his own medicine and planned how he'd make the Captain walk the plank, cast him adrift in an open boat, steal back his treasure and banish him forever. Sadly Jack was prey to feeling queazy on the briny and so far he has hardly caught a glimpse of the Captain's ship!

Jack came to Colour Box via a Hugglets Teddy Festival.

Code: TC228
Issued: Jun 1993
Issue Price: £9.99

Code: TC227
Issued: Mar 1993
Issue Price: £9.99

Teddy Bears Collection

KING WILHELM II

Code: TC229
Issued: Sept 1993
Issue Price: £9.99

No-one was absolutely sure what had happened to King Wilhelm I; King Wilhelm II himself was very old and he couldn't remember! In fact that was Wilhelm's trouble — he was extremely forgetful. Sometimes he got up in the mornings and went into the royal dressing room to fetch his regal scarlet sash and by the time he'd got there he simply couldn't remember what he'd gone in to collect! Then there was the day he left his crown on a Number 18 bus! Luckily the bus conductor returned it safely to him. But no-one minded that he forgot their names or their birthdays because he always remembered his manners!

Code: TC230
Issued: Jul 1994
Issue Price: £10.95

NICHOLAS

One of four bears that bring back memories for Peter and Frances of being in the Baden-Powell organisations years ago. Nicholas is the Boy Scout (see also Colin, Victoria and Muriel). Some bears automatically take charge of a situation and keep calm in a crisis and one such bear is Nicholas. Tracking was always one of his favourite subjects and he spent a long time studying the different paw prints of animals in the snow or mud. He is also a good cook, creating exciting meals for the rest of his Boy Scout troop who are all very pleased when Nicholas's name appears on the list for making the campside supper.

Code: TC231
Issued: Jul 1994
Issue Price: £10.95

VICTORIA

Victoria was always a very energetic bear. She did all kinds of outside activities and even liked the more rugged pursuits! When she joined the Guides, she started to do those things she liked best and went away every year to summer camp. It nearly always rained on at least one day, but Victoria was never put off and liked the long walks and cooking round the stove in the evenings.
Victoria is the Girl Guide of the four Baden-Powell bears. See also Muriel, Nicholas and Colin.

Teddy Bears Collection

TRICK-CYCLIST

Code: TC232
Issued: Jul 1994
Issue Price: £10.95

BERTIE

*B*ertie could never make up his mind! It had always been a problem for him but try as he might he always found it impossible to make a decision about anything — especially if he was in a hurry! He had spent most of his childhood on a farm in the South East of England. The little girl he lived with loved the outdoor life and spent much of her time in the garden or playing in the orchard where her daddy grew apples. She always had questions for Bertie like whether he preferred red apples or green apples, whether he liked daisies or buttercups and whether he preferred orange juice or cola. In the end, all her questions left him quite perplexed and unable to make up his mind. Even years afterwards when Peter Fagan asked him if he would care to join the collection, Bertie had to think hard and eventually decided it would be fun, if he could have some peace from being asked questions!

Code: TC233
Issued: Feb 1995
Issue Price: £11.25

ON THE ICE

Code: TC234
Issued: July 1995
Issue Price: £11.25
No picture available prior to publication

*W*orld champions on ice, two of Peter Fagan's bears are skating to victory and entertaining the crowds. They have practised throughout the cold months on the village pond which stays frozen over for most of the winter and can take all kinds of leaps and twirls. When they first tried their dance routine on the ice at the ice rink with some music, the effect was quite spectacular! They discovered a new world of smooth movement and colour and had a wonderful time working out how to fill the space and finish the dance. Eventually, with their routine perfected, they decided to try for the big competition . . . . .

SCHUBERT

Code: TC235
Issued: July 1995
Issue Price: £11.25

No picture available prior to publication

35

CARLO

Code: TC236
Issued: July 1995
Issue Price: £11.25
No picture available prior to publication

*N*o-one could ever doubt that Carlo is a showman of a bear! He wears a collar of bells so that everyone can hear when he's coming and he is especially proud of his red silk sash. He says he was given it by an Italian acrobat who also gave him his name. Carlo lived for quite some time with the Italian acrobats who toured Europe giving shows in the streets for pennies. He never quite managed to tumble over himself, but he often took part in shows by sitting next to the hat at the end and helping to collect the wages. After a while the acrobats moved on and Carlo was left with a family in Holland. From there he came into the hands of Peter Fagan who recognised his character at once and resolved to bring him back to Scotland.

NANA

Code: TC237
Issued: Feb 1995
Issue Price: £11.25

A soft, gentle and quiet bear, Nana had been at school for years. She had belonged to Miss Hamilton, a gentle and sensitive lady who ran the local Primary School. Sometimes, the infants would gather in the foyer at the end of the corridor and at times it was noisy chaos until Miss Hamilton positioned herself in the middle. With one finger on her lips she could silence the entire crowd in a matter of seconds. If children were good they were allowed to go to Miss Hamilton's office and the best treat was to tell Nana the bear what they had done. If Nana was pleased then Miss Hamilton would issue a paper star and stick it in a book. There were different coloured stars, best of all were the silver and gold ones!
Nana is one of numerous bears purchased by the Fagans from a Hugglets Teddy Festival in London.

LIBEARTY

Code: TC238
Issued: Feb 1995
Issue Price: £11.25

*L*ibearty was commissioned by the charity *The World Society for the Protection of Animals* as part of the 'Libearty' campaign and features a wild bruin. The piece is intended to help raise public awareness and funds for the charity whose work protects the lives of real bears endangered by extinction and cruelty wherever they may be found. A donation of 7.5% of Colour Box's trade price on every bear sold will be donated to WSPA.

36

Code: TC310
Issued: 1988
Retired: 1992
Issue Price: £8.75

HIGHLAND LADDIE

*P*eter Bear, named after his new master, comes from a Scottish background. Starting life in Glasgow, he travelled the Highlands and Islands and eventually arrived at a sale room in Edinburgh, where he was to become the first in Peter Fagan's family of teddies. A 1/1 Limited Edition of Highland Laddie was cast in solid gold in 1988; see Golden Bear in 'Rare and Unreleased Pieces' of Section Three.

Code: TC311
Issued: 1988
Retired: 1990
Issue Price: £8.75

THE ACADEMIC

*T*his is none other than August String-Bear reading up on the work of his (almost) namesake. The specs were purchased for 10 Francs by Peter during a holiday in Northern France and were included to help August tackle the smaller print (he's an aged bear and a little short-sighted).

Code: TC312
Issued: 1988
Retired: 1990
Issue Price: £8

LAP OF LUXURY

*D*uring a house move in 1988, Frances discovered her own bear, Teddy Robinson, in an old trunk. Feeling very guilty about shutting her away for all those years, Frances "made a special bed for her on a cushion and opened a box of sweeties to share! The fact was that our cat at that time simply loved chocolate and ate most of the box of sweets himself." The moment was recorded by Peter in a model: Teddy Robinson as she should be, in the "Lap of Luxury."

ARTISTIC LICENCE

Code: TC314
Issued: 1988
Retired: 1991
Issue Price: £8.99

THE QUIET LIFE

T he bear enjoying 'the quiet life' is Bruno. The marking on this piece reads: '© PF '89'; however, it is rather indistinct on some pieces.

Code: TC315
Issued: 1989
Retired: 1993
Issue Price: £17.50

Code: TC316
Issued: 1991
Retired: Spring 1995
Issue Price: £14.50

NORMAN

N orman lost his ears one dreadful day when he was hung out to dry on the clothes line after suffering the indignity of a bubble bath. As it was extremely windy he was flung about until both his ears became dislodged. He was given a corduroy replacement set of which he was very ashamed. To cover his embarrassment he acquired a smart cap which he had seen fast bike riders wearing and as a result he became interested in the sport. He can now be seen "pulling wheelies" in the front yard, cap askew, dungarees flapping and thoroughly enjoying himself!

Code: TC320
Issued: Mar 1992
Issue Price: £4.99

EDUCATING TIMMY

I n order to be educated correctly, Timmy has to be cast separately in production and glued onto his school bench!

KENNY

*K*enny was the mascot of a young man called Sam who lived in Kensington and who thought up the name "Kenny" since that was where they lived! Kenny stayed in the flat all day, but every night it was something different: a work-out at the gym, a game of squash or an exhausting hour on the walking machine. Kenny enjoyed keeping fit and keeping Sam company. It was Sam's mother who had knitted Kenny a smart red and blue tracksuit to match Sam's.

ARABELLA

*S*uch a romantic! So passionate and elegant, Arabella dreams of roses. She sat for years in the corner of the garden room in an elegant house in Bromsgrove whilst her mistress wrote long and passionate letters to her sweetheart. Arabella loved the writing paper which was kept in the bureau drawer. It was tinted a most delicate shade of pink and was hidden underneath a lace sachet of dried, perfumed rose buds so that each sheet was steeped in the soft summer fragrance. Nowadays she has turned her attentions to Peter Fagan who did give her the rose she wears and who is also a romantic at heart.

MORRIS MINOR

*F*irst day at school is enough to make anyone feel nervous and Morris Minor was no exception. He had packed a satchel but left it at home in his rush for the school bus, his ink pen leaked in his pocket, and his half-sucked gobstopper had fallen through the hole in his pocket lining. Never mind, Morris Minor loved school and lived in the desk of his best friend, Colin. There were many educational adventures before Morris Minor met Peter Fagan who, as someone who hasn't completely grown up yet, immediately appreciated Morris's character!

39

REGINA

Regina lived in a pet shop in a London suburb called Palmers Green. It was an old-fashioned shop with sawdust scattered over a black and white tiled floor. Every corner of the shop was crammed full of bird cages and fish tanks, pet beds and baskets. The ceiling was festooned with bundles of millet, cuttlefish and squeaky rubber bones. There was a smell of dog biscuits and caged mice and the shop was invariably full of children who came in to see what was new.

A colourway was issued in 1994 in the USA as part of the Pennywhistle Lane collection.

Code: TC324
Issued: Mar 1992
Retired: 1994
Issue Price: £4.99

RAZZA

Razza was over-excited. Razza was always out of breath. Razza couldn't ever manage to calm down. The shop that bought him thought he was a dog,and then a lion — others thought he was a hyena! — but the little girl who bought him knew he was a bear. Razza always wanted to make her laugh and he played whizzo tricks, pulled funny faces and when she grew up and got married he even sat in the front seat of the wedding car wearing the chauffeur's hat!

The real Razza was purchased by Frances and Peter Fagan at a Christie's auction.

Code: TC325
Issued: Mar 1992
Retired: Spring 1995
Issue Price: £4.99

BEATRICE

Beatrice suffered from freezing paws, largely because she spent most of her working life in a chilly art studio that was once an old gatehouse. The main house had been turned into a school and Beatrice was the companion of the eccentric art mistress, Miss Seward. An icy wind penetrated every corner of the gatehouse and Beatrice's paws suffered , until one day Miss Seward popped her into an old hot water bottle cover which served as a sort of sleeping bag!

Code: TC326
Issued: Mar 1992
Retired: 1994
Issue Price: £4.99

NOLAN PORRIDGE

Code: TC327
Issued: Jun 1992
Issue Price: £4.99

Nolan was the name of the boy with whom Nolan Porridge lived and he called him 'Porridge' because of what he had for breakfast! Nolan Porridge had lead a rather boring life, sitting alone in the bedroom. Then one day he was taken to an Oxfam shop and an elderly lady bought him. She was a lollipop lady and for years Nolan Porridge helped stop the traffic for schoolchildren. He was never bored again and met hundreds of friends who called him "Lollipop Bear".

SULLIVAN

Sullivan lived in Ireland for the first few years of his life before moving to Manchester. The family he lived with had a baby, and one day the baby dropped Sullivan out of the pram on their way to school. Sullivan was picked up by a lorry driver and hitched a lift in the cab. He spent a long time travelling about the country before finally ending up in London at an auction. Sullivan also has a cousin in the Colour Box collection — Shiner.
A Sullivan colourway was created for a promotion at 'Just Right' (or in Welsh 'I'r Dim') in Denbigh to celebrate the shop's tenth anniversary in 1993. His jersey was painted in bands of red, green and white (the colours of URDD, a Welsh Youth Organisation) and with the name 'I'r Dim'. Leftover Sullivan colourways were offered to Club members via the Club magazine.

Code: TC328
Issued: Jun 1992
Retired: 1994
Issue Price: £4.99

Code: TC329
Issued: Jun 1992
Retired: 1993
Issue Price: £4.99

PHILIP

Philip Pettigrew Proudfoot, OBE, is an eccentric bear. He received the OBE (Order of the Bear Essentials) for his services to ornithology. "Pippit" is how he is known to his friends and members of the bird-watching club for whom he had become a type of mascot. He has kept a careful note of all his sightings since he joined the club and is particularly proud of his record of the nesting habits of the Crested Grebe, documented in full with diagrams. A particular, meticulous mind, a keen eye and a nimble frame, all qualities of a real natural scientist.
Both Philip and Sullivan were purchased from Christie's in London.

RED BEAR

Code: TC330
Issued: Jun 1992
Retired: 1994
Issue Price: £4.99

*R*ed Bear started life in a nursery in a large house in the north of England. He had been given to a small boy called Michael one Christmas. Sadly Red Bear never felt especially loved, and when then the family moved to Kent he ended up in cupboard. By this time the family had a baby girl called Pamela and a new Nanny had been taken on who came from Switzerland. The Nanny found Michael's Red Bear in the cupboard. She called him "Le Petit Ours Rouge" (which is French for Little Red Bear) and began to tell stories of Red Bear's adventures during those missing years. She wrote the stories in a book and many years later both Red Bear and the book came into the hands of Peter Fagan.

Code: TC331
Issued: Mar 1993
Issue Price: £4.99

MEEKIE

*M*eekie was a bit of a misfit. He had been made out of a scrap of reddish-coloured cotton fluffy stuff and his eyes were leftover green plastic eyes from a sewing kit that made up a frog! He was for sale on a charity stall but he looked so spooky that no-one wanted him . . . until a little girl called Katherine came along. When she saw Meekie she used every penny of her pocket money to buy him. When they got home Katherine found her dolly's duffle coat was a perfect fit and Meekie was happy at last with his new friend, never to be a misfit again!

Code: TC332
Issued: Jun 1993
Issue Price: £4.99

VERNON

*V*ernon was a cheerful, caring teddy who had been made out of an old piece of greenish cotton material that an old lady had found. His cardigan had been specially knitted for him. It was a bit big but Vernon didn't mind. He loved party games and Hide and Seek was his favourite which he used to play with his own ted . . .

IAN

Code: TC333
Issued: Sept 1993
Issue Price: £4.99

*T*he friendly smile, the cheeky sideways glance of this optimistic little bear proves he is a character of good humour. He stayed for many years in a house that stood on the banks of the River Forth with a little boy who grew up to become a bank manager. One day Ian was whisked away to an airy office where he sat on the window sill listening to the little boy he once knew, now grown up and wearing a smart suit. The pretty young ladies in the bank gave Ian his lovely blue bow and he wore it with pride as he smiled at all the customers.

Like so many Colour Box bears, the real Ian was purchased at Christie's in London.

Code: TC334
Issued: Mar 1994
Issue Price: £5.50

PRISCILLA

*P*riscilla had been a little self conscious about her new green paws since having her paw pads replaced and she wasn't at all sure that she like them.   Then one day she discovered a new and really rather delightful talent. She had noticed the dead leaves on one of the indoor plants in the conservatory and picked off all the brown ones. The plants began to flourish and before long Priscilla had acquired the reputation of being a particularly good indoor gardener. Then she realised that she had new green paws and that was why she must be so good with plants!

JINGLES
(or Jingles Better Bear)

Code: TC335
Issued: Mar 1994
Issue Price: £5.50

*J*ingles Better (or just Jingles for short) *has suffered in his little life — bumps and grazes almost everywhere. He lost an eye and completely lost an ear and even spent some time in hospital once when he needed an operation. The wonderful thing about Jingles is that he keeps cheerful and brave and never complains. If you feel down in the dumps, under the weather or have an accident, think of Jingles and let him bring you a bit of better luck to cheer you up. Sometimes it's hard to be brave and you need a friend to help and that is just what Jingles does best!*

Jingles was discovered in a very sorry state in the viewing room of Christie's auction house. In fact he was overlooked by Peter and Frances Fagan; but he caught the eye of Colour Box's Marketing Manager, Joan Walker-Alton, and Sales Manager, Ingrid Gitsham, who took great pity on him and persuaded (or should that be 'pestered'?) the Fagans into buying him. Anyway, their determination was commemorated in the new bear's name — 'J' for Joan + 'Ing' for Ingrid = 'Jing-les'!

REGGIE WHISTLER

Code: TC336
Issued: Mar 1994
Issue Price: £5.50

*R*eggie spent many years living in a block of flats where there were a lot of children and a small dog. The only way the small dog could be made to behave was when the master or mistress whistled. When everyone had gone to work and school the dog simply went back to being naughty, so Reggie decided he would have to learn to whistle. No matter how hard he tried, the sound just wouldn't come and the dog still remained very disobedient, until one day he found a small wooden whistle in one of the children's pencil cases. When Reggie blew the whistle, the dog immediately did as he was told and Reggie was delighted. In fact he was so pleased that he tied the whistle round his neck so it would be handy whenever he needed it. Reggie Whistler came from the 1993 Hugglets Teddy Festival in London, and his name was created by some of the Colour Box collectors. In fact quite a number of Colour Box bears have originated from Hugglets festivals over the years!

NYM

Code: TC337
Issued: Mar 1994
Issue Price: £5.50

*M*ost bears have a burning ambition and Nym discovered from an early age that his passion was the Ballet! He had seen a small part of Tchaikovsky's Swan Lake on the television once, and since then he simply yearned to leap about and throw ballerinas into the air like thistledown. His mixed coloured fur coat made him look quite the part to go on stage and he often performs for the other bears in Peter Fagan's collection, although he is still waiting to be discovered by the Royal Ballet!

Code: TC338
Issued: Mar 1993
Issue Price: £5.50

LITMUS

*I*f ever you studied chemistry you'd know that Litmus is a very special sort of paper that changes colour when you dip it into different things. Litmus bear was so called because he changed very quickly once, from a Victorian table cloth into a bear! Quite a dramatic change, hence he was christened Litmus.

COLIN

Code: TC339
Issued: Jul 1994
Issue Price: £5.50

*H*ave you ever found a frog in your sleeping bag? If you have, then maybe you've been camping with Colin! of course some people think Colin is a bit on the naughty side, but he's never really done any harm despite his mischievous sense of humour and most people forgive him for his jokes. Colin the Cub Scout, one of the four Baden-Powell bears — the other three are Nicholas, Victoria and Muriel. Every time one of these Colour Box miniatures is sold, a donation is made to the relevant Baden-Powell organisation.

MURIEL

Code: TC340
Issued: Jul 1994
Issue Price: £5.50

*M*uriel was a very determined bear. Anything she set her mind to was sure to happen. She loved badges and joined the Brownies as soon as she could so that she could start to work towards all the awards she longed to achieve. And as a Brownie she was always hard at work helping people.
Representing the Brownies in the Baden-Powell bears is Muriel. The other three are Victoria, Colin and Nicholas. The original bears sculpted by Peter were dressed by Collectors Club member Frances Sadler, a seamstress who was herself a Guide and researched the uniforms for accuracy. Peter's originals were then checked with the Baden-Powell organisations and slight modifications made to the masters (hat badges, shoulder insignia, woggles etc.) prior to production.

STRIP

Code: TC341
Issued: Jul 1994
Issue Price: £5.50

*W*hen Strip was very young he lived in Germany but when an American tourist bought him in a toy shop in Denkendorf he began a long journey over the sea to America. He had never dreamt how America would be. All the way over the sea in the huge liner he tried to picture his new home and when he first caught a glimpse of New York harbour he knew he was just going to love it. Strip really enjoyed living there on the shores of a big lake in a town called Chicago. When his family eventually all grew up he was left for sale in an antique toy store which led to a flight back to Europe and a new life with Peter Fagan.

Code: TC342
Issued: Jul 1994
Issue Price: £5.50

PAISLEY'S BOOT

DANIEL

Code: TC343
Issued: Jul 1995
Issue Price: £5.75
No picture available prior to publication

*D*aniel enjoys messing about in boats. It all started when he was taken down the river with his family for a picnic. They had hired a rowing boat from the little wooden pier and set off in the warm sun. He was fascinated by the sound of the gentle water lapping up the side of the boat. There were ducks and moorhens near the banks and they even saw what the family thought was a water rat dart up the bank into a hole. Daniel has a dream that one day he would own a rowing boat of his own. It would have to be smaller than the real one because he wouldn't be able to reach the oars but he hoped that perhaps someone would make him one.

BO

*B*o prefers to sleep during the day. Teddy bears are not, of course, naturally nocturnal but Bo has a very good reason for preferring to remain alert at night. He is a passionate star-gazer and his great love is to wait until dusk when the stars start to shine and then Bo gets out his telescope and looks at as many constellations as he can from behind the clouds. He had the surprise of his life one night when he saw a shooting star. His friends told him, that was a good luck sign and ever since then he's been looking for another one. His life long ambition is to see a star that no-one else has seen before and have it name after him. (Someone told him once that great astronomers lent their names to stars.)

Code: TC344
Issued: Feb 1995
Issue Price: £5.75

PETER BEAR

*N*amed after his current owner, Peter Bear is a solid, reliable, Scottish bear and the founder member of the Colour Box collection. Frances Fagan recalls vividly her first meeting with him: *"When we had our first house, like most new couples we didn't have any furniture and we had to go out and buy the basic things for our home. Peter is not the most organised of people and he decided to spend some time hunting round the antique shops in Edinburgh as he much prefers old things to modern ones. I thought that he'd gone hunting for a table and chairs, and when I arrived home I was eagerly awaiting to have a meal comfortably, instead of sitting on the floor! I couldn't believe my eyes when he came in with a china cheese dish under one arm and Peter Bear under the other! He was triumphant! "I've had a marvellous day," he gleefully said. "Look at these." Peter Bear sat staring at me from the crook of Peter's arm and since we were having spaghetti for tea I couldn't begin to understand the reason for the cheese dish! However, Peter Bear was a real friend to us and soon joined us on the floor for our evening meal and even slept on the bed. A friend of mine whom I had taught to spin made Peter Bear a little Shetland scarf and as he lived with us it was not long before Peter decided that he wanted more bears to join the family."*

PETER BEAR

Code: TC410
Issued: 1988
Issue Price: £3

ROBERT

*R*obert (pronounced "Ro-Bear" as in French) started life in a toy factory out-side Paris just after the First World War. He lived in Paris for the early years of his life but travelled into Belgium through Brussels and eventually arrived in a sale room in Bruges where he was purchased by the owners of The Curios Shop. He was sold to Peter Fagan in the summer of 1987 and has lived with him ever since. Robert is a gentle, generous bear with an optimistic outlook on life and a smile for every-one. This secret expression is unique to Robert and is what has made him one of Peter's most cherished friends.

Code: TC411
Issued: 1988
Retired: Spring 1995
Issue Price: £3

AUGUST STRING-BEAR

*A*ugust String-Bear, like the playwright after whom he is named, Auguste Strindberg, is a philosophical charac-ter. Born in Germany in 1908, he moved to Sweden during the Inter-War years. He suf-fered from mistreatment in his early life and this, together with a natural reticence, has made him something of an introvert. His res-cue from an unhappy youth into the intel-lectual surroundings of University life in Berlin gave him his interest in the arts and philosophy. An accidental journey through Europe left him in Ypres during the Second World War from where he travelled to Bruges, ending up in the Curios Shop where Peter Fagan purchased him in 1987. August String-Bear appears in a number of Peter's sculptures (e.g. The Academic, Boxing Day).

Code: TC412
Issued: 1988
Retired: 1993
Issue Price: £3

GUSTAV VON BRUIN

Code: TC413
Issued: 1988
Retired: 1994
Issue Price: £3

A German aristocrat, Gustav boasts a musical background. His birth in the early 1920s is sadly unrecorded, but it is known that he moved to Austria where he spent much of his youth and early middle age as the mascot of the Austrian Orchestra, at the School of Music in Leipzig. During a tour of capital cities, he was lost in Brussels and then travelled (by mistake) onto Bruges where he was sold to the Curios Shop in the summer of 1986. The following year, Peter Fagan discovered the shop and the rest, as they say, is history . . .

Code: TC414
Issued: 1988
Retired: 1994
Issue Price: £3

DICKIE BEAR

D ickie is the American Colour Box Bear. He came to England from America in 1986 and started life in a gift shop in upstate New York. Whilst Frances was in a business meeting in a boutique (she used to make designer knitwear) Peter took her small son Paul for a walk and returned to the shop with an enormous smile on his face. He was carrying a bag and out of the top Frances could sea a pair of furry ears. They belonged to Dickie Bear who had apparently accosted Peter in a nearby gift shop and expressed a wish to come to England to trace his roots!

Code: TC415
Issued: 1988
Issue Price: £3

CHRISTOPHER BEAR

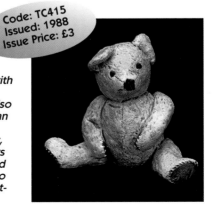

C hristopher Bear is a kind-hearted Irish rogue with a twinkle in his eye.
Christopher was Peter's father's name and is also Peter's middle name; he's very much one of the Fagan family and one of Peter's favourites. Peter's family came from Ireland (from Galway) and, coincidentally, so did Christopher Bear. He belonged for many years to the Captain of an Irish tugboat. He was discovered in a shop in Edinburgh, sitting on a high shelf, next to an old and well loved Golly. Peter and Frances adopted both, as they were clearly friends.

Teddy Bears Collection

HUMPHREY

Code: TC416
Issued: 1989
Retired: Spring 1995
Issue Price: £3.50

*H*umphrey was born in 1957 and lived in a large roomy house in Chelsea. The attic was converted into a nursery and Humphrey lived up high with an excellent view of the locality. In 1969 he moved to Salisbury to live in a beautiful house in the Cathedral Close, where he was happy for many years. A large and lovable bear of little conversation but much consideration, Humphrey is always slow to comment upon the actions of others but he is always very caring, particularly with the younger, smaller bears.

Humphrey also has another identity — for when he dons his protecting helmet and clothing he becomes Safety Ted!

BRUNO

Code: TC417
Issued: 1989
Issue Price: £3.50

*B*runo comes from humble beginnings in a poor but loving family in the Midlands. Born in 1947 his happy early days were with his first little girl who found him a great comfort as her parents had been separated by war.

He spent his older years in the West Country with a very old lady whose pride was her cottage garden and he learnt much of the outdoor life, but after her death he was given to a charity shop and sadly his next family were none too caring. He lost his eyes and nose and eventually was given away, ending up in the flea market in Romsey where Peter adopted him.

Frances Fagan: "The first time we saw Bruno he was in a sorry state. He had been bundled into the bottom of a glass case in a flea market in the town of Romsey in Hampshire, near where we used to live. Poor Bruno, he had no eyes, nose or mouth and had clearly been sadly neglected.

Despite his appearance we took him home and I set to work to put him right. Lucy and I sorted through the button box and found two suitable black buttons that we sewed on for eyes. I then had to fashion a nose and mouth and when he was finished he looked really rather friendly. To add a touch of colour we then sorted out the yarn box and I knitted him a multi-coloured scarf."

A colourway Bruno with a red and white scarf was produced in October 1993 for Lincoln Co-op.

RALPH

Code: TC418
Issued: 1990
Retired: 1994
Issue Price: £2.50

*I*n the days when a gentleman always wore a button hole and carried a silk kerchief in his pocket, Ralph the Bear would enjoy the high society life of old London town. The streets were lit by flickering gas lamps, casting pools of yellow light in the London fog, as Ralph waited at the stage door with flowers for the leading lady. His latter years were spent much in reflection of his sparkling early days as he sat in the window of his terraced house in Bath, dreaming of tea at The Ritz and spring walks in Green Park. He was to meet Peter much later, in a country antique shop which Peter frequented. On one trip, to examine a Grandfather clock, Ralph was introduced to him and they became firm friends.

SOPWITH

*S*opwith was a young aviator; driven by a passion for flying, he lived with his friend and hero Second Lieutenant Arthur Turnbull of the Royal Flying Corps, who made his way up the ranks until his tragic death in a DH5 at 3 Training Depot Station, Netheravon, on Salisbury Plain. Sopwith's real name is Edward Bear, but a competition was held to select a nickname for him when he entered the Colour Box collection: Isobel Cameron from Edinburgh was the winner ('Sopwith' is actually the surname name of a pioneer aircraft designer). Sopwith still looks to the skies for his inspiration, although his flying is now strictly limited to passenger aircraft. He dreams of the days when he could hear the rattling engines of a De Havilland aircraft as they spun high in the air above Salisbury Plain and shares his memories with other bears in Peter's family.

Code: TC419
Issued: 1990
Retired: 1994
Issue Price: £2.50

KLIM

*K*lim is a powerful, athletic bear with a passion for cycling, and quite a hero amongst the Colour Box bears. One of them, Irvine, had a dream that one day he would win the Milk Race, but his legs were too short to reach the pedals of a racing bike; so when Klim signed up to ride in the 1992 Milk Race, he said he would win it for Irvine! He sports the winner's yellow jersey and special cap and carries an important snack in his back pocket. (All Milk Race riders eat bananas!) Peter sculpted Klim as the official mascot of the 35th Milk Race, held in England and Wales during May and June 1992 — hence his bright yellow winner's jersey. Klim also appeared on the Colour Box Milk Race trophy presented to the race winner, Connor Henry. Such was Klim's popularity that he stayed on to support the 1993 Milk Race and a teddy Klim trophy was again presented to the overall winner, Chris Lilleywhite. Why 'KLIM'? Think 'MILK' backwards!

Code: TC422
Issued: Mar 1992
Retired: 1993
Issue Price: £9.99

TICK TOCK TED

*T*ick Tock Ted lived with Professor Kasselhof who was an expert horologist. There were so many clocks in the house where he lived that there was very little room for anything else! The collection was mostly made up of chiming clocks and every quarter-hour the house rang with a mixture of bells, gongs and pretty tunes. But it was the hourly stroke that really shook the foundations, as the clocks never told the exact time and the striking bells seemed to ring out for several minutes. This is why Tick Tock Ted now feels quite at home with Peter Fagan, who has a passion for striking clocks and who allows Tick Tock Ted to assist him when winding up the two grandfather clocks which stand in the hall.

Code: TC430
Issued: Sept 1991
Issue Price: £2.99

BEN

*B*en had a bookshop in a tiny lane in the quiet end of Exeter. Sometimes he was reached down and put into the hands of a child whose parents had come in to browse. One day a small child "borrowed" him and he went to live in a hotel in Lyme Regis where he met Binkie Bear. They became firm friends. Eventually they were auctioned in London. Ben was sold first and thought he would never see Binkie again, but luckily Peter Fagan adopted them both! A colourway of Ben is marketed in the USA as part of the Pennywhistle Lane collection.

Code: TC450
Issued: 1991
Issue Price: £2.99

BINKIE

*B*inkie started life as a prize in a fairground at a coastal resort. He then lived for some years in a big white hotel in Lyme Regis with an old lady and some other bears, including a small bear called Ben. One day a trip to London brought them to a prestigious auction room. Ben and Binkie had to part company because they were put into two different sales, but as fate would have it Peter Fagan adopted both of them and were reunited. Binkie is one of Peter's friendliest little bears and is a great favourite with everyone.

Ben and Binkie did indeed come to Colour Box via an auction room — Christie's — and Davey was purchased on the same day. Although the story of Binkie was created by Frances Fagan (based solely on memories of passing signposts to Lyme Regis on her way to and from university in Exeter), a Colour Box collector wrote to Frances claiming she knew the hotel in question and had stayed there years before! The collector even travelled to Lyme Regis, tracked down the white hotel and asked the proprietor if he knew anything about the teddies. He said no . . . but added that the previous owner, an elderly lady, had collected bears and they had been sold at auction up in London! In the USA a colourway of this piece is available as part of the Pennywhistle Lane collection, with an accidental spelling change — Binky.

Code: TC451
Issued: 1991
Issue Price: £3

DAVEY

Code: TC452
Issued: 1991
Issue Price: £3

Davey Bear is a dreamer. His first dream was to be big, but it never came true. He lived with his friend Robert McQueen in a small town north of Brighton. Robert was a dreamer too, he wanted a red tractor and dreamt about driving one, but Davey just dreamt about being big. He joined up with Peter Fagan long after Robert McQueen drove a real tractor and Peter and Davey share their dreams together. Davey has never grown big; he is small and friendly with his head in the clouds and his heart in the right place.

The real Davey was purchased at Christie's in London, at the same time as Binkie and Ben. A colourway of Davey with brighter colours on his waistcoat is available in the USA as part of the Pennywhistle Lane collection.

Code: TC453
Issued: 1991
Retired: 1994
Issue Price: £2.99

IRVINE

Irvine is mad about bikes. He used to belong to a girl called Jo who lived in Suffolk and they went on many rides together, with Irvine sitting on the back and clutching on for dear life. Irvine always carried his "useful things" bag in which he kept his puncture repair outfit, an egg sandwich and a clean handkerchief. Sadly Jo and Irvine parted company one day when Irvine fell off the back of the bike, which led him via all kinds of adventures to Peter Fagan.

MR PERKINS

Code: TC456
Issued: 1991
Issue Price: £3

Just as it is with people, some bears who are more cheerful than others, and Mr Perkins is one of them. No matter if it rained on his birthday or next door's dog dug up the geraniums, Mr Perkins always managed a smile. As a young bear he lived in Bradford and can remember the days when the mills were all busy and the smell of hot wet wool and chemicals seemed to pervade every corner. He retired to the Derbyshire hills to indulge his favourite pastime, following the streams amongst the granite boulders and smelling the sweet open air.

CHOCOLATE CHIP

Code: TC457
Issued: 1988
Issue Price: £3

*A*s his name suggests, Chocolate Chip is small and sweet. He has a nervous disposition and suffers from agrophobia (fear of open spaces) and he worked hard to pluck up courage to leave the nursery! He lived in Cheltenham but because of his affliction Chocolate Chip never went far from the house and garden. However, that didn't mean that he led an uninteresting life. Indeed, he had quite an experience once on a visit to the Zoo, but that is another story . . .
The real Chocolate Chip was purchased at a Christie's auction. A colourway Chocolate Chip was produced in September 1992 for Cottage Crafts, Sawbridgeworth.

Code: TC458
Issued: 1991
Retired: Spring 1995
Issue Price: £2.99

SHINER

A well-meaning bear with an enthusiastic nature but rather accident-prone and inclined to get over-excited! He lived in a council house in Epping with a boy called Oliver who was also accident prone. Once Shiner got caught in the brambles whilst blackberrying and during the rescue he was catapulted into the air and got stuck in a tree! He met Peter in a London saleroom and as soon as Peter walked past, Shiner characteristically leapt off the shelf into his arms.
Like his cousin Sullivan, the real Shiner came to the Fagans via Christie's in London.

TINKER THOMAS

*T*inker Thomas was a gift one Christmas to a small gypsy boy who lived in a caravan and only seldom went to school. A farmer's wife had given Tinker Thomas to the child out of pity for what would have been a poor Christmas otherwise. He lived in the bright painted gypsy caravan which roamed the New Forest. The caravan was mostly green with red floral and other wonderful bright patterns all over it. It was pulled by a small brown New Forest pony called Casper. There were not many gypsies left in the Forest and the time inevitably came when the family were settled into a cottage and the caravan ended up in a museum. Tinker was rescued, came to London and thus met Peter Fagan.

Code: TC459
Issued: Sept 1991
Issue Price: £2.99

PAUL

Code: TC460
Issued: Jun 1992
Issue Price: £2.99

*P*aul Bear was called after the little boy who looked after him. The "real" Paul was small, blond and mischievous. They lived in a country house on the side of a hill with a big garden. Paul would sit his bear in the back of his red push-along tractor as he played in the yard at the side of the house. Both Pauls would play happily together until one dreadful day, Paul (the bear) got left by mistake on a bus and ended up in a lost luggage office. Many adventures followed before he met Peter Fagan and was given a new blue ribbon and a place in the Colour Box hug.

Code: TC461
Issued: Jun 1992
Issue Price: £2.99

VIOLET

*V*iolet is a very quiet bear. She has lived so long in the public library that she is hardly used to loud noises. Every day she went to the public library by bus and sat on the counter helping to sort the tickets and stamp the books in and out. She loved to watch the people choosing what to take out and the researchers ploughing through the dusty volumes that were not to be removed on loan. She enjoyed the children's corner, although there was often a bit too much noise as the clamouring youngsters read aloud from bright picture books.

SQUIDGE

Code: TC462
Issued: Jun 1992
Issue Price: £2.99

*S*quidge belonged to a small boy called Howard who was always playing practical jokes on people — a bag of flower on top of a door, a rolling skate on the stairs. Squidge was always squeezed close to Howard's chest and this is why he has a slightly flattened nose, because he has spent his life trying to watch Howard's jokes from the grip of his tight embrace. When Howard grew up, Squidge was given to the local hospital where he met Teddy Randell. After a hospital sale, the two bears luckily went together to a different home where Squidge found a new pal called Grant. Eventually Squidge and Teddy Randell were both adopted by Peter Fagan.

POPSEY

Code: TC463
Issued: Oct 1992
Retired: 1994
Issue Price: £2.99

One of the quietest and most shy of all the Colour Box bears is Popsey . He finds it very difficult to talk easily to strangers and is always very wary of new places and social events. He collects what used to be called cigarette cards, but they are now found in teabag boxes. He sticks them in a big album with coloured sugar paper pages. He prefers wildlife pictures to any others, particularly butterflies.

Popsey first appeared in the Colour Box collection in 1991 as Party Bear (XTC419) complete with Christmas trimmings (cracker etc.). These were removed when he became plain Popsey in 1992. Then, in the original festive format, he was reissued in 1994 in the USA as part of the Pennywhistle Lane collection, not under the name Party Bear . . . but Popsey. (Confused? If so, re-read.) See also James. During pre-production, two colours were used to paint Popsey's body, and a few pieces may have been released in this two-tone style. However, this was changed to one colour for ease of painting.

Code: TC464
Issued: Oct 1992
Retired: 1994
Issue Price: £2.99

JAMES

James loves all things that are traditionally English. He lives in a beautiful Georgian town house on the North East coast of England, almost on the Scottish Border. He enjoys the garden (especially the climbing roses), he collects fine old English procelain and Chippendale furniture, and gets particularly excited about cricket. There is nothing he loves more than to sit on the edge of the village green on a warm Sunday afternoon and watch the local team gently bat themsleves towards the tea pavilion, where James always settles on the wicker armchair for a cup of tea before the walk home.

James first appeared in the Colour Box collection in 1991 as Present Time (XTC418) with the addition of a Christmas stocking and a collar. In this festive format, but still named James, he was reissued in 1994 in the USA as part of the Pennywhistle Lane collection. See also Popsey.

FRED

Code: TC465
Issued: Mar 1993
Issue Price: £2.99

Fred lived with a little boy called Christopher and they were the best of friends. Fred went everywhere with Christopher and whatever happened to Christopher also happened to Fred. One day Christopher became rather ill and Fred went with him to hospital. Fred didn't mind helping Christopher to feel better as he felt he would have liked to have been a doctor if he hadn't been a teddy! A colourway of Fred with was produced in September 1993 for Choice, Welwyn.

Code: TC466
Issued: Sept 1993
Issue Price: £2.99

BURT

One day Burt was travelling on the London underground with Dorothy, his best friend. When Dorothy got up to get off the train, Burt tumbled out of her bag and fell down the gap between the train and the platform. Dorothy didn't notice and Burt lay there for ages until an engineer who was mending the lines rescued him. He was given to the ticket collector who displayed him in the ticket office for a long time, just in case his former owner came back that way. After several months he became a sort of mascot for the station and was given a special underground badge.

BABY BEAR

The youngest teddy of all of Peter Fagan's bears is Baby Bear. He really is too immature to leave on his own and all the other bears help to look after him. He lived in a cottage in Dorset with a little girl called Karen who made him wear a nappy and pushed him around in a big black pram that she used to have when she was a baby. It was in the doctors' waiting room, one day, that Baby Bear was given his little teething toy. Karen found it at the bottom of the toy box that was always under the waiting room table. Baby Bear was so pleased with his new toy that the kind receptionist said he and Karen could keep it, and although Baby Bear is older now he has never really grown up.

Code: TC467
Issued: Feb 1995
Issue Price: £3.50

HENRY

Code: TC468
Issued: Feb 1995
Issue Price: £3.50

*H*enry hasn't been able to hear properly since he lost his outside ears. He still has what he calls his 'inside ears' which help him to remember what sounds are like, but he can't hear every tiny sound any more. He still manages to keep cheerful even though he is hard of hearing and always has a smile for everyone. If he concentrates hard he can see what they are saying by recognising the shape of the words on their lips, which is really very clever. The other bears in Peter Fagan's family help Henry enormously by speaking slowly and clearly and not putting their paws in front of their mouths when they talk to him. He doesn't like people shouting, he just wants people to understand.

Code: TC469
Issued: Feb 1995
Issue Price: £3.50

BANANA LEE

A bear with more bounce would be hard to find! Banana Lee is a yellow bear, just exactly the colour of ripe bananas (without the black spots). He has a passion for sunshine and outdoor activities and is never still for more than a minute. Banana Lee lived in one of the playgrounds of the world! He was brought up in Florida and everyone was always on to him about how he should prefer oranges to bananas, but Banana Lee wouldn't change his mind. He loved the beach best and sat for hours with his friend, whose name was also Lee only she was a girl! They would lie in the sun for ages. Banana Lee never changed colour but Lee herself went browner and browner! Banana Lee was introduced to Peter Fagan and persuaded him to bring him back to Scotland where he was given his red silk ruff. Now he brings some life and colour into the lives of all Peter's bears.

BOBBY

*B*obby lived in the kitchen for most of the time, that is, he was a sort of mascot belonging to a chef in a little restaurant in a seaside town on the North East coast of England. He didn't have much expertise himself, but he enjoyed watching Chef put some exciting ingredients together and especially liked the way Chef made each plate look so attractive with the decorations of flowers cut from tomatoes and little feathery bits of fennel. The best part of any meal, as far as Bobby could make out, was the dessert. There was always a magnificent dessert trolley, piled high with all kinds of majestic confections. Bobby watched with fascination when Chef spun the sugar into delicate webs of glistening threads and balanced them over mounds of soft creamy mousse . . . . Delicious!

Code: TC470
Issued: Feb 1995
Issue Price: £3.50

Teddy Bears Collection

PEREGRINE

Code: TC510
Issued: 1988
Retired: Spring 1995
Issue Price: £1.75

*P*eregrine was born into the aristocracy of London's St. James's Square in 1935. He spent his` early youth in the green perambulator with his master and mistress going for walks with their Nanny. He spent some time with them until he was dropped from his pram in Hyde Park. He lived a varied life but was never again to find a life of idle luxury. Learning much of the poorer side of London society, he eventually was stolen away to sea and traversed Northern Europe. Despite language difficulties Peregrine was eventually sold to a Belgian dealer and ended up in the Curios Shop in 1987 where he was purchased by Peter Fagan.*

TEDDY ROBINSON

Code: TC511
Issued: 1988
Issue Price: 1.75

*T*eddy Robinson was Frances Fagan's own bear when she was little and unlike most teddies she has a tail! She stayed with Frances from the age of about three until she was eighteen as they both grew up together in North London. Frances then left home to go to university and Teddy Robinson was packed away in a trunk and put in a storeroom, only to be rediscovered many years later. Her redemption is the subject of another piece — Lap of Luxury (TC312).*

Teddy Robinson is not, as some collectors might imagine, named after the series of children's books by Joan G. Robinson featuring a bear of the same name. Frances Fagan never read the books as a girl and the names are coincidental. She also discovered recently that Joan Robinson was also brought up in North London and in similar family circumstances to herself!

THEODORE

Code: TC512
Issued: 1988
Retired: 1994
Issue Price: £1.99

*T*heodore is the oldest bear in the collection, having started life with a little girl in Canada in 1907. He was reunited with his long time mistress, Miss E.W.D. Steel, in 1989 and she narrated to Frances Fagan the remarkable details of his life: Paris in the 1930s, internment during the war years; a witness at an important gestapo trial; strafed by the RAF who mistook the train on which he was travelling for an enemy troop train; helping to find the families of misplaced persons after the war; caring for old people; being sold at Christie's to raise money for charity and thus meeting Peter! In fact it was an article in a Scottish newspaper about Theodore's wartime history and his sale that first inspired Peter and Frances to visit Christie's. They ended up purchasing the very bear they had read about and since then Christie's has been the source of many new additions to the Colour Box collection.*

Code: TC513
Issued: 1988
Retired: 1994
Issue Price: £1.99

JOHANN

*J*ohann is a tiny bear but he has a long and interesting tale to tell. He spent his early youth in a quiet country house in France, but had much medical assistance, since he suffered from a bad chest complaint. He went with the little girl, who was his earliest companion, to a sanatorium in the Black Forest from where he was to 'return with the brother of 'his' little girl. Sadly, Johann never saw his mistress again. His new friend took him into Paris where the joyous evenings by the river and the friendly nightlife with the artists and showmen amused him a great deal. It was with the outbreak of the Second World War that his travels began again and after a terrible experience in occupied Paris Johann made his escape to Belgium where he was to live with a craftsman and lutemaker. His enjoyment of the soft ethereal instrument added calm to his later years before his trip to Bruges and the dark corner of the Curios Shop. Peter has given him his own miniature lute, an antique tortoiseshell one, inlaid with pearl. Perhaps not so exquisite a piece of marquetry as he was used to, but it has been much appreciated.

VERNON'S TED

*V*ernon's Ted is Vernon's best friend. Both bears lived with a little girl called Katherine and all three were often playing Hide and Seek. During one game Vernon's Ted fell into an old oak drawer just as Vernon and Katherine were closing their eyes and he lay there, upside down, for an hour and a half before they found him!

Code: TC514
Issued: Jun 1993
Issue Price: £1.75

PAISLEY (Pink & Blue)

A very quiet, shy bear whose job it was to comfort a tiny baby called Bobby. He had been called Paisley because Bobby's granny always wore a beautiful Paisley shawl whenever it was chilly. Paisley had been bought ready for Bobby before he was born and as Bobby's granny didn't know whether the baby was to be a boy or a girl, she had bought two ribbons for Paisley, a pink one and a blue one. To this day, Paisley can still wear either and look just as smart!

Code: TC515 (Pink)
TC516 (Blue)
Issued: Mar 1993
Issue Price: £1.75

BLITZ

Code: TC517
Issued: Sept 1993
Issue Price: £1.75

*D*uring the Second World War, Blitz had lived in London with a family who had six children. When the bombs came in the darkness, the house Blitz lived in was badly damaged one night. The family escaped to the underground shelter but Blitz was left in the rubble, with one eye broken in half and both ears gone. Luckily an air raid warden found her, put her in his pocket and took her home. His wife used two old sock toes to make new ears and Blitz lived happily with the couple until she was put up for adoption and came to live with Peter Fagan. There she acquired a new green pinafore dress, made specially for her by Frances Fagan.

BEEZER

Code: TC518
Issued: Mar 1993
Issue Price: 1.75

*B*eezer lived in a beach hut in St. Mary's Bay. She had lived there for as long as she could remember with a man called Doug. Doug had found Beezer after a long summer day on the beach. Everyone had gone home and Beezer was under a tin bucket until Doug discovered her in the sand. Doug looked after the deck chairs and Beezer's job was to guard the orange cash tin where he kept his change. During the winter, Beezer went to help in the the cafe in the town and sat on the counter as Doug served at the tables and cleared up at closing time.

COUSIN ECCY

Code: TC519
Issued: Sept 1993
Issue Price: £1.75

*C*ousin Eccy lived in a plating works in Sheffield where cutlery is cast and plated with silver. Eccy worked in the accounts office and spent most of his time helping the book-keeper with his addition. He sat on the desk watching his friend Tom copy lists of items into the huge ledger in beautiful spidery copper plate writing. Cousin Eccy hardly ever visited the foundry but when he did he watched the craftsmen making special castings in sand moulds. It was on a business trip to London that he found his cousin Fluffy and was very excited to hear about the Colour Box bears. So when Eccy retired he knew just where to come.

JOSEPH

Code: TC520
Issued: Sept 1993
Issue Price: £2.99

*J*oseph lived in a cupboard for the whole week and
only came out on Sunday afternoons when lots of
children came to the village hall for Sunday School.
Then it was his turn to have some fun as the toy box
came out just before storytime. His favourite story was
about a young man who was also called Joseph and who
had an absolutely fantastic coat, just like a rainbow.
Joseph bear wished and wished that one day he would
have a coat of many colours just like Joseph in the story.
He did have a little red vest but that wasn't quite the
same somehow.

Code: TC522
Issued: Sept 1993
Issue Price: £1.75

POLSKA

*P*olska was a refugee. He had come over to England
after the Second World War having left Poland during those troubled days. He didn't speak much
English and has had to study hard to get used to his new
home. Back in Poland he used to live in a sausage factory
and his passion for Polish dry sausage has never left him.
He like them sliced up and fried. Polska's favourite pastime is to throw a midnight party and since he came to
join the Colour Box hug of bears he has often led a night
time raiding party down to the kitchen, leaving a great
deal to clear up in the morning!

Code: TC523
Issued: Mar 1994
Issue Price: £1.99

NORBERT

*A*my Jackson found Norbert in a dustbin at her
school in Spalding, Lincolnshire (hence the
school tie), and he was sent to Peter because
no one could decide who should take him home.
Peter duly sculpted his miniature and in March 1994
visited the school and presented the first Colour Box
Norberts as a gift to each child in the school. No
prizes for guessing the name of the school . . . St.
Norbert's!

CHLOE

Code: TC524
Issued: Mar 1994
Issue Price: £1.99

*C*hloe is a very shy bear, she is constantly aware of her small size and worries a great deal about getting lost. She had an unfortunate experience once on a green-line coach. She had been travelling with her friend Josephine all day on the bus when it went over a pothole and everything landed on the floor with a bump, including Chloe! She had rolled right under the seat in front and, while the family spent all day on the beach, Chloe was miserable on the floor of the coach waiting for them to come back. When it was nearly dark she heard footsteps and voices and saw to her relief the smiling face of Josephine staring at her. So Chloe was rescued, a bit dusty but safe and sound.

PINKY

Code: TC525
Issued: July 1995
Issue Price: £1.99

*P*inky the small pink bear was so-named because that was what she cost! Anna was only seven and was preparing for her school jumble sale. She and her class mates had been gathering together lots of odds and ends, old toys and clothes that they no longer needed. All the junk and jumble was put in huge heaps in the school hall. The toy pile was the biggest and the most interesting. Anna and her friends were allowed to help set out the toys on the day before the sale. They were busy opening the bags and boxes and Anna discovered in one bag a small pink bear. The bear wasn't very pretty but Anna thought it was wonderful. Miss Watson, Anna's teacher, could see Anna was very excited and asked her if she's like to have first pick, before the sale. Anna was delighted and chose the pink bear, putting one shiny penny in the old tin box.

Code: TC609
Issued: June1992
Retired: Spring 1995
Issue Price: £1.49

MINI-MIDGE

*M*ini-Midge loved her housework. She gloried in dusting, revelled in polishing, enthused over washing up and positively excelled herself at clearing out cupboards. She lived in a large stone house in a bleak northern town where it was still customary to be up at dawn and polishing the door knockers before breakfast. Mini-Midge is a bear of strict domestic routine and rarely deviated from a day spent devoted to housework and tidying. She kept her favourite duster in a small bag that never left her side.

FLUFFY

Code: TC610
Issued: 1988
Retired: 1993
Issue Price: £1.15

Frances Fagan has a remarkable true story to tell about Fluffy :
"Although Fluffy always looks a little sad, his story has a very happy ending. As a little girl I had lots of teddies and Fluffy was added to my collection when I was just seven. By the time I was twelve or thirteen I was foolish enough to think that I was too old for teddies and so I gave a good many of them away, including Fluffy. I thought no more about it for many years and through my teens we moved across London. Eventually I left home. All my toys were packed into the attic. Like most students I used to return from University for the holiday times when I was roped into helping with my father's school jumble sale. It was my job to clear up all the rubbish and as I was sweeping the school floor, what should I find in the middle of the heap of rubbish but a small Teddy! Feeling rather sorry for it, I picked it up — and to my amazement it turned out to be my Fluffy, whom I had given away when I was only twelve! What had happened to him in those six or seven years between is a mystery to me, but I'm quite sure he must have got up to a lot of adventures! As you can imagine I was absolutely delighted to have him back and although he still looked a little sad, he is my favourite bear because he found me after all those years."

JONATHAN

Peter and Frances once lived in Hampshire, and it was there they discovered Jonathan, at an antique fair in a local hotel. Jonathan had lived in rural Hampshire all his life and spent the first ten years on a smallholding just outside Lyndhurst in the New Forest. He then moved to Lymington, a coastal town, also in Hampshire. On a beach picnic one day, he had been helping with a sand castle competition and was put down behind a particularly large castle. The worst happened: he was left behind. He stayed on the beach all night before being picked up by a fisherman. Great efforts were made to trace his family, but no luck. Eventually he was sold to an antique dealer who took him to the Sunday Antique Market where Peter saw him.

BRODERICK

Much of Broderick's life was been spent on an old steam line in Monmouth and the Welsh Valleys. He lived in the verdant Wye Valley and was used to a fair bit of rain. Broderick used to sit high above the dials watching the crew shovel coal into the boiler at high speeds, flying over the viaduct that hovered above his favourite valleys. Sadly the line is now closed and the magical roar of the great iron dragon, as Broderick fancied the engine to be, is silenced for ever.

Like so many Colour Box Bears, he arrived via an auction house and was acquired at the same time as Bernard, the Cockney bruin. To achieve the unusual darkened mohair effect, a special colour had to be mixed for Broderick by Colour Box's master painter, Terry Fairbairn. The colour has since been used on other pieces.

Code: TC611
Issued: 1988
Retired: Spring 1995
Issue Price: £1.15

Code: TC612
Issued: 1990
Retired: 1994
Issue Price: £4

Code: TC613
Issued: 1990
Retired: 1994
Issue Price: £4

BERNARD

*B*ernard was born in Cockney London Town in the 'Roaring Twenties'. He had always been a jovial bear and soon made quite a name for himself in the night-clubs of London where he lived. Eventually he moved back to the East End to help his family with their barrow stall which they ran in Covent Garden market. When the 'real' market closed in Covent Garden, he moved across town and settled down in the Soho district on the Piccadilly side. Eventually he made his way to a London saleroom where his enormous lively amber eyes caught sight of Peter Fagan and they instantly became friends. Bernard has remained a par-ticular favourite of Peter's because of his warm and wel-coming personality.

JILLY BEAR

*W*arm in her country farmhouse kitchen with the smell of new baked bread pervading the old stone house, we find Jilly Bear. She lived all her life on a quiet farm nestling in a river val-ley in the Scottish Borders. The quiet river, a tributary of the Tweed, flowed past the back garden where there was always washing on the line. Jilly's best love was baking day, always a Friday, ready for the family at the weekend. Jilly would be found decked in her green apron, deep in the old flour-crock, baking the scones for tea. She has dedicated her life to pleasing others and takes great pride in looking after everyone. She now helps and protects the younger bears in Peter's family and is always ready to assist in the kitchen.

A colourway of Jilly Bear with a different coloured apron was produced in October 1992 for Owen Owen.

Code: TC614
Issued: 1990
Retired: 1994
Issue Price: £5

ROGER

*R*oger has led a wonderfully exciting life. It began quietly in a London sub-urb but took a turn one day when quite by chance he became the mascot to a hospital ambulance. Whizzing through the busy streets with sirens and lights flashing on wonderful rescue missions, Roger was an essential member of the team. He was espe-cially helpful if any children had to be taken on board as he would sit patiently helping them to be brave. He retired from the ambu-lance team when he was permanently adopted by one little girl who needed his help to get better. She let him join Peter and the other Colour Box Bears when she had recovered so that he could continue to share his strength of character with others.

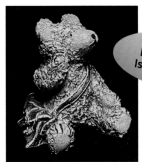

Code: TC615
Issued: 1990
Issue Price: £5

TIMMY

A quiet bear of timid disposition, Timmy is very shy, but extremely intelligent. Timmy was once a glorious golden mohair bear of very high quality with shining boot button eyes. he was the very proud acquaintance of a small boy who simply 'loved him till he was bald.' Timmy has always been very nervous of loud noises and is particularly sensitive to thunder storms. He spent many a stormy night buried deep under the covers sheltering from the lightening. He acquired his lovely red jacket one afternoon at a school sports day when his lack of fur left him quite chilly, and he was treated to a new red coat; red being his favourite colour.

Code: TC616
Issued: 1990
Retired: 1994
Issue Price: £5

BERTRAM

Code: TC617
Issued: 1988
Issue Price: £4

B ertram remembers the Empire! The days when geography lessons consisted of listing all the 'pink bits' on the map and remembering the Commonwealth. Life was so much simpler then for a very patriotic bear. Bertram started life in York, a truly historic city. He would tour around in a local bus and enjoyed many visits to the Minster. At the time of the Coronation he came to London and when he walked in the procession he was jostled and caught up in the crowd. He was picked up by a   roadsweeper and given to a schoolgirl, it was at this time that he was presented with his scarf bearing the crown and initials of the King. Bertram is a Royalist and enjoys everything to do with the Royal family, especially weddings and new Royal babies! It will come as no surprise to learn that Bertram's birthday is 23rd April — St. George's Day!

JIMMY

Code: TC618
Issued: Sept 1991
Retired: Spring 1995
Issue Price: £4.85

J immy was champion at building sandcastles. His passion for the beach had begun when he was young and has grown over the years. He lived in Bournemouth, near the beach where his family ran a fish and chip shop that was open all hours to tourists and locals alike. Jimmy liked the days when coachloads of holidaymakers arrived in the town. He had his family would often walk down to the beach where the children could play and where Jimmy could help with the sandcastles. Now he lives by the sea with Peter Fagan and still makes many trips to the beach with Peter's family.

GEORGE

Code: TC619
Issued: Sept 1991
Issue Price: £4.85

*G*eorge lived in a London public house for most of his life and spent nearly every night on top of the piano as his friend and master 'tickled the ivories'. George loved the music hall songs best, his favourite being the one about the Nightingale in Berkeley Square.

A colourway with a red waistcoat (it's usually light brown) was produced over Christmas and New Year 1993 for selected Lawleys Stores. Another version, with a green waistcoat and 'K & S' in gold letters was produced in December 1993 for Kircaldie & Staimes in New Zealand. A colourway is also marketed in the USA as part of the Pennywhistle Lane collection.

CHIEFY FRASER

Code: TC620
Issued: Sept 1991
Issue Price: £5

*L*ike Sopwith, Chiefy Fraser is also an aviator bear. 'Chiefy' is only a nickname for Flight Sergeant Fraser Bear, the mascot of the RAF Engineers who serviced the planes at Drem during the Second World War. Frances Fagan acquired Chiefy Fraser at a Christies auction — the first time she had had to bid without Peter — and she was drawn to him by his Air Force uniform. When it was Chiefy's turn to go under the hammer, she raised her hand nervously and swallowed hard. The bidding went high but Frances had already decided there was no way she was going home without him, and so she did! When she examined him after the sale, she noticed his toy watch which was tucked in his pocket. The time read 11.10, almost exactly the time that she had bought him! A double coincidence awaited her when she got Chiefy home and sat him next to Tick Tock Ted, who wears a real (broken) watch around his neck. Tick Tock Ted's watch also reads 11.10!

DAMIEN (Red, Blue or Turquoise Coat)

Code: Red Coat TC621;
Blue Coat TC622;
Turquoise Coat TC623
Issued: late 1991
Retired: 1994
Issue Price: £4.85

*D*amien is very particular about his appearance. He had acquired this reputation in the theatre dressing rooms when he had been the boudoir companion to a particularly well-known actress of the stage and music hall. He rarely watched the performance because his role as official companion (no-one has 'mascots' in the professional theatre, he was told . . .), meant that he had to sit in the dressing room. Damien has three different theatre costumes. His first choice is the shining turquoise but he is just as comfortable in his pillar box red or delphinium blue silk jackets. It was, in fact, his change of costume that brought Damien and Peter Fagan together, but that is another story . . .

WILLIAM

Code: TC624
Issued: Mar 1992
Retired: Spring 1995
Issue Price: £5.99

William Gladstone Faulkener Herd is a splendid Highland bear. He is proud of his Scottish heritage and has been a very supportive clansman. He spent most of his youth in a small croft on the west coast but did travel south on one notable occasion to visit relatives! He has a passion for tartan, bagpipes and haggis. He celebrates Burns' Night with gusto and regularly walks the purple, heather-clad hills of his home.

PRUDENCE

Code: TC625
Issued: Mar 1992
Issue Price: £5.99

Prudence tended the Vicarage garden in Lower Stanbridge-on-Aye. She used to belong to the sister of the young vicar who had recently moved to the parish. Prudence spent her days in the house or garden assisting with such things as flower arranging and pricking out marigold seeds. Gentle and generous, Prudence is a most modest bear and not one to be pushy or outspoken. She has a relative in the Colour Box collection — Cousin Fergus.

Several colourways of Prudence have been produced: 1) red trim to hat and dress for Glorious Britain, Gatwick Airport, July 1993; 2) for Choice, Welwyn, September 1993; 3) pink dress with white edging in November 1993 for Lynne's Cards and Gifts, Woking, November 1993; 4) colourway for the USA — see Pennywhistle Lane collection. Peter Fagan used a rosette touchmark on this figurine.

Code: TC626
Issued: Mar 1992
Retired: 1994
Issue Price: £5.99

CLARISSA

When Peter Fagan found Clarissa in a lot of bears at an auction, she was damaged almost beyond repair. She had lost her paws, one leg had been pulled off, both eyes twisted out and she had been left for rubbish. But Peter saw that she was a bear of great family history and pride, and he had her restored to her original beauty, including a new pair of blue glass eyes the colour of sapphires. Then she paid a visit to Mrs Turnbull who designed and knitted her a gorgeous outfit. Now Clarissa is better, her old self again.
Clarissa is a Christie's bear.

67

Teddy Bears Collection (vertical side text)

EMLYN

Code: TC627
Issued: Oct 1992
Retired: Spring 1995
Issue Price: £5.99

*T*he Welsh National Opera has inspired many music lovers, but none so dedicated as Emlyn. Coming from the town of Prestatyn in North Wales, he has been a devout follower of the Welsh musical tradition with a special love of Welsh male voice choirs. When still quite young, Emlyn went to live in Bristol and in later life developed an interest in antique books and old gramophone records. In the Colour Box hug, he became firm friends with Ben, who also knows a great deal about old books, and Gustav Von Bruin, Peter Fagan's most knowledgeable musical bear.

This bear first made an appearance in the Colour Box collection in 1991 as Mistletoe Bear (XTC218) and was remodelled without festive trimmings before release as Emlyn.

STANLEY

Code: TC628
Issued: Jun 1993
Issue Price: £5.99

*B*ased on a Steiff bear who arrived at Colour Box in a very sorry state, with hardly any stuffing left and hardly any face, Stanley spent most of his extraordinary life of travel and trauma travelling up and down the Nile river in North Africa. Although he was overworked and the weather took its toll, Stanley was thoroughly restored by teddy doctor Brian Beacock before Peter set to work sculpting his miniature. Stanley returned to the Nile with Frances and Peter in 1994 and had his picture taken at the Pyramids (see from cover of Collections and Reflections No. 27 for proof!).

A colourway of Stanley with green and red waistcoat was produced in November 1993 for Randles, Wellingborough. In the USA Stanley is marketed as part of the Pennywhistle Lane collection.

LALLY

Code: TC629
Issued: Mar 1993
Issue Price: £5.99

*L*ally had a vivid imagination. Ever since she was a cub she used to make up stories. Her paw-writing was never very good and quite a lot of her letters came out backwards but her stories were exciting and full of lively chatter. She loved romantic tales of times gone by and invented all kinds of characters. She made everyday things come to life and breathed life into mundane objects which seemed to jump off their shelves to join her stories. In 1994 real romance entered her life; Lally was whisked away to Gretna Green by Miles the promotion bear where they were secretly married!

TEDDY ESCU

Code: TC630
Issued: Mar 1993
Issue Price: £5.99

*T*eddy Escu started life in Holland where he was just called Teddy. Then one day his family saw very sad pictures of little children in Romania who needed help and he was packed away with some other toys and sent across Europe to Orphanage 5 in Bucharest. The doctors there were pleased to get parcels, but the children needed food and milk and warm clothes more than toys. So Teddy was sent to London to be sold at auction and it was there that Peter Fagan adopted him. The money raised by the sale was sent back to Romania where it was used to buy the children new cots. Teddy Escu's new name came from the Romanian children and he is certainly very proud to have helped.

Code: TC631
Issued: Sept 1993
Issue Price: £5.99

ADRIAN

*A*lthough Adrian is wearing his pyjamas, he is in fact a bear who is used to getting up early. Most days he's out of bed at the crack of dawn and dives into the cab of the white transit which takes him to work. Adrian assists a firm of decorators and spends a lot of time watching the team transform people's homes. The best bit is stripping walls; Adrian really enjoys helping to rip off old paper and slosh the paste in the bucket for the new. Very occasionally he gets in the way and once he was dripped with white undercoat which had to be washed off.

Prior to release, the stripes on Adrian's pyjama were spaced further apart as they proved too difficult to paint accurately.

Code: TC632
Issued: Sept 1993
Issue Price: £5.99

ELLY MAY

*E*lly May has been called the mother to all new Colour Box Teds and looks after every newcomer with such gentleness and welcome that no-one feels left out. Elly May wanted a huge family but she lived for many years on her own with an old lady in America. She wished she could have had dozens of children to play with but it was not to be until she moved to England where she sought her roots amongst the farming community in Devon.

A colourway of Elly May with a salmon/pink check coat instead of the usual white with blue and red flowers and a brown bow was created for a promotion at 'Cameo House', Chesham, Bucks, in June 1994.

Code: TC633
Issued: Mar 1994
Issue Price: £6.75

DIM SUM

*T*he name doesn't really indicate Dim Sum's true nature. After all he is of royal descent from the rare Emperors of China who ruled centuries ago. Dim Sum, so named after Peter Fagan's favourite hors d'oeuvres at the local Chinese restaurant, was far from being dim and really could not be compared to the steaming pork dumpling after which he had been named. In fact Dim Sum is a truly wise and royal panda and well versed in the rules of royal etiquette and good manners. He is rather slow at some things but he could never be considered dim even at the worst of times.

The original bear was purchased by Peter and Frances at the 1993 Hugglets Teddy Festival in London.

Code: TC634
Issued: Mar 1994
Issue Price: £6.75

COUSIN FERGUS

*C*ousin Fergus stays in a grand Georgian town house on the outskirts of the city of Edinburgh. He enjoys a brisk walk down the Queensferry Road and into town where he goes shopping in Princes Street and often takes a turn around the Gardens. He likes to be in town at lunchtime because he always listens out for the one o'clock gun. Fergus has a cousin in the Colour Box hug, Prudence, who lived in an English vicarage.

Code: TC635
Issued: Mar 1994
Issue Price: £6.75

SKIPPER

*S*kipper has been a captain for only a short time but no-one is sure exactly what sort of vessel is under his care. Is it a ship or a plane or a bus? No-one has ever known exactly and no-one has ever had the courage to ask. Since Skipper is covered in silver braid, all the other bears believed him to be a very important high-ranking official, and so he is.

GABRIEL

Code: TC636
Issued: Jul 1994
Issue Price: £6.75

Gabriel belonged to a small boy called Colin Gabriel and because of his name Gabriel Bear was a star in the school nativity play every year (though he would have preferred to play a king!). After many years of playing the angel, Gabriel was put away in a cupboard and rarely came out to play as Colin grew up and moved away. Eventually he came to live with Peter Fagan and was delighted to be made so welcome. Now he is proud to play his part in the teddy bears' Christmas story.

ALICE

Code: TC637
Issued: Feb 1995
Issue Price: £6.95

Always the beautiful bridesmaid, but not yet the blushing bride, Alice is dressed for a wedding in her special peach satin dress that matches the flowers in the church. Alice was delighted when she was asked to be a bridesmaid. She wasn't sure what that meant but she soon discovered that she could help choose a new dress. She was told that peach was to be the special colour and everything should go with that from the buttonholes to the ribbons on the handles of the car. Alice was driven in a wonderful shiney black car, with ribbons, and she had never had such a good day. Being a bridesmaid is a lot of responsibility for a bear and Alice did her duties well. She wants to do it again soon, although she really would prefer to be the bride. Now that she lives with Peter Fagan's teddy bear collection, who knows, but she might find romance of her own one day.

MARCUS
Code: TC638
Issued: Jul 1995
Issue Price: £6.95
No picture available prior to publication

Marcus has a favourite game; he likes to play soldiers! When he first went to live with his close friend Graham, a six year old boy with bright red hair and freckles, Marcus wasn't at all sure if he was going to have fun, but he soon changed his mind when he saw Graham's toy fort. The soldiers were rather a mixture and included some old flat tin ones that had belonged to Graham's dad, a few plastic Cowboys and Indians, two black and white cows and a giraffe! Graham dressed Marcus as a soldier and both friends spent hours re-enacting famous battles together. Only when Graham had long grown up and gone to college did Marcus leave home and join the ranks in Peter Fagan's teddy collection.

LITMUS MAGIC

Code: TC639
Issued: Jul 1995
Issue Price: £6.95
No picture available prior to publication

NYM'S SURPRISE

Code: TC640
Issued: Jul 1995
Issue Price: £6.95
No picture available prior to publication

IRVINE'S TREAT

Code: TC641
Issued: Jul 1995
Issue Price: £6.95
No picture available prior to publication

BINKIE'S PUMPKIN

Code: TC642
Issued: Jul 1995
Issue Price: £6.95
No picture available prior to publication

BARROW BOY

Code: TC700
Issued: Feb 1991
Retired: 1994
Issue Price: £29

OH! MR PORTER

*O*n the luggage trolley is Broderick, the bear who spent much of his life on a steam line in the Wye Valley, hence the sheen of coal dust that has darkened his fur. Here he can be seen daydreaming about the wonder of taking control of one of his beloved steam engines. For practical reasons, the bear was cast separately during production.

Code: TC701
Issued: Sept 1991
Retired: 1994
Issue Price: £29

73

Code: TC800
Issued: Sept 1991
Retired: Spring 1995
Issue Price: £4.85

DEREK

*F*or many years Derek lived at the Post Office. He had been en route as a Christmas present to a boy called Alistair Carnforth but had parted company with his wrapping, and consequently Alistair's address. So he took up residence in the Sorting Office until a real stroke of luck reunited him with his rightful family. Eventually he met Peter and joined the collection.

BARON VON BERNE

*D*espite his grand title, this bear is really quite approachable and prefers to be called simply 'Baron'. He can trace his aristocratic lineage in Europe through three centuries. Baron travelled across Europe with his family on a tour and was left in London after an evening at the Ritz, which is how he finally ended up at an auction where he met Peter. They struck up an immediate friendship.

A colourway of Baron Von Berne with green and silver hat was produced in April 1993 for a Lawleys Collectors Weekend.

Code: TC801
Issued: 1991
Issue Price: £4.85

BRODIE

Code: TC802
Issued: Sept 1991
Retired: Spring 1995
Issue Price: £4.85

*B*rodie was for many years the personal mascot of a young Lieutenant Colonel in the Coldstream Guards and spent much of his life in the beautiful Scottish Borders. He then went to London and had a long spell in the barracks near Buckingham Palace. When his friend and colleague eventually retired from the service, Brodie enjoyed a number of adventures in the City before meeting Peter at a sale auction. He arrived with a squashed nose and without a mouth; his stuffing had also shifted, giving the appearance of not having a neck. He has since enjoyed a major refit! He is named after a friend of Lucy Fagan's at her playschool. For a two-day shop promotion in November 1994 to celebrate the centenary of Henry Clark Ltd., one of Colour Box's stockists in Leicestershire, a special colourway of Brodie was created with a blue scarf and the name of the store. The scarf is usually grey.

Teddy Bears Collection

The Collectors Club & Limited Editions

THE COLOUR BOX COLLECTORS CLUB

Launched in 1987, the Colour Box Collectors Club was initially administered by Jane and Dave Allan, friends of Peter Fagan's, who also ran a smallholding in the Borders. They produced a modest black & white newsletter called The Colour Box Collector, corresponded with collectors and organised the despatch of Club pieces and offers.

The Club was a success from the start. Member No.1, Mark Peck, was recruited in June 1987, and such was the speed at which membership increased that in early 1990 Susan Hargreaves became the 10,000th member. In early 1995 the total number of recruits was well on its way to 50,000.

The first colour newsletter appeared in summer 1989 and it was about this time that the Allans relinquished control of a Club which had become administratively very demanding. Peter Fagan's wife Frances had been helping with Club matters from the beginning, contributing articles for the newsletter and corresponding with collectors; she now became editor of the newsletter and also adopted responsibility for the management of the Collectors Club. Being so close to Peter there could be no better person to offer an insight into his work.

In 1991 the newsletter transformed into a magazine proper with 24 glossy pages of news, information and competitions for collectors. It also acquired a name — Collections and Reflections — chosen from collectors suggestions in a competition in the newsletter. For the first time the magazine was also made available to non-Club members with a cover price of £1.00. In March 1995 the magazine increased to 32 pages.

Probably the greatest attractions of Club membership are the complimentary gift piece and the opportunity to purchase pieces sculpted by Peter Fagan exclusively for Club members.

CLUB PIECES

Listed here are the pieces offered to Club members as a complimentary gift on either joining for the first time or renewing their membership. However, 1995/96 heralds a new idea which breaks with this established tradition — see Opening Night.

Code: CC87
Issued: June 1987
Retired: May 1988

BLACKBOARD

Blackboard also exists as a shop point of sale (see section on Other Items) and features Hopscotch characters Plain Cat (H2) and Teddy Bear (H40).

EASEL

Issued: June 1988
Retired: May 1989

ATTIC

The old picture frame is one Peter remembers used to be stored higgledepiggledy with other pieces of bric-a-brac in the family loft.

Issued: June 1989
Retired: May 1990

NOTICE BOARD

At the bottom of the lane where Peter lived as a boy was the old church, on the little village green. On the edge of the green stood the Parish Notice Board with news and happenings in the village pinned up for all to see. This is Peter's memory of the board, complete with his pet cat, a cheeky little bird and Johann bear.

Issued: June 1990
Retired: May 1991

WALL

The wall in question is the wall that surrounded the big house where one of Peter's boyhood friends, Morris, lived. Peter would visit Morris every weekend, and part of the four mile journey involved a short cut over 'the wall'. Note the broken bricks that made excellent footholds!

Issued: June 1991
Retired: May 1992

Club and Limited Editions

76

CHALKBOARD

*T*his piece takes Peter back to his own primary school days in Essex. He was never very academic but in his first school report his headmistress said he was very good with plasticine and enjoyed modelling!

Issued: June 1992
Retired: May 1993

BILLBOARD

*P*eter used to do a paper round years ago, and every morning he would lean his bike on the old billboard outside the local paper shop. Although Peter's little dog wasn't quite the same breed as the puppy in this piece, he used to hide under the old billboard in just the same way. Also hiding under the billboard is Tinker Thomas.

Issued: June 1993
Retired: May 1994

Issued: June 1994
Retired: May 1996

OPENING NIGHT

*T*here are two mould versions of this piece. In Mould 1 the diamonds on the curtains are freehand painted on, whereas in Mould 2 they are cut into the mould as a guide for homepainters. The first version is also more elaborately painted, with flowers on the stage, multicoloured letters in the word 'Collections' and patterns on either side of the words 'Peter Fagan'. These are all missing on the second version.

Opening Night is the complimentary piece for all Club members (new and renewing) between June 1994 and May 1995. It is also the complimentary piece for *new* members joining between June '95 and May '96. However, *renewing* members for the '95/'96 year have the choice of three pieces, one for each of the main collections of Teddy Bears, Home Sweet Home and Pennywhistle Lane. Collectors who would like to add more than one to their collection can purchase the other two at cost price.

THE ARTIST

Renewal item for Teddy collectors: June 1995 - May 1996

CLUB OFFERS

Club Offers are pieces offered for purchase exclusively by Collectors Club members. The first three items (two specially sculpted pieces, Decorative Cat [see A Collectors Guide to Home Sweet Home], Silver Miniatures and Theodore's Pastimes) were made available directly from the Colour Box Club Office. Thereafter pieces have been ordered from retailers by presenting a Redemption Certificate supplied with the Club newsletter/magazine.

THEODORES PASTIMES

The original Theodore was auctioned at Christies by his owner specifically to raise money for the charity "Research into Ageing". Inspired by this generosity, Peter decided to sculpt a piece featuring Theodore and to donate 15% of all sales to R.I.A. A cheque for £1,500 was sent to them, as reported in Club Newsletter No. 11 (summer 1990). Supplied with a wooden plinth.

Issued: Spring 1990
Issue Price: £12

SILVER MINIATURES

Issued: 1989
Issue Price:
Cat & Ball £25;
Mini Teddy £21.

Two models from the Hopscotch Collection were produced in solid sterling silver — Mini Teddy (H40) and Cat & Ball (H56). Though strictly not relevant to this book, they are mentioned as one of them was a teddy bear.

LIFEGUARD

Featuring Christopher Bear (TC415) with special rubber ring and captain's hat.

Issued: March — August 1991
Issue Price: £6.95
Edition Size: 3,000

TIME FOR REFLECTION

Featuring Bertram, Colour Box's patriotic bear, sitting on his park bench dreaming about the days of the Empire.

Issued: Sept 1991 — February 1992
Issue Price: £20.95

PICNIC PUSS

Issued: March — August 1992
Issue Price: £20

Two mischievous felines can be seen creating havoc with an al fresco lunch!

Issued: March — August 1992
Issue Price: £10.95

OUT FOR A RUN

This piece features Jimmy, the beach bear from the fish and chip shop, out for a morning jog before the holiday makers arrive.

SAIL AWAY

Code: CC931S
Issued: August 1993 —
March 1994
Issue Price: £19.99

SOPWITH'S SOLO FLIGHT ▼

The original Sopwith bear was awarded his wings in 1992 having flown in an RAF Tornado jet (over Lauder amongst other places), his first flight for 75 years. Subsequently Peter and Frances bought him a radio-controlled model of an SE5, the kind of plane he had flown in with his owner during World War I, so that he could make his first ever solo flight. This duly occurred on 2nd April 1994, and Peter immortalised this momentous occasion in an aviator bear's life by sculpting this magnificent piece. The actual flight can be seen on the Colour Box video, The Story So Far . . ., and it raised money for the Children's Hospice Association Scotland.

The aeroplane's fuselage is cast in two sections which are then glued together. On the first models produced, the cut was made lengthways (creating a top and bottom), but this was soon changed to a vertical cut (creating a front and back).

Code: CC932S
Issued: April 1994 —
March 1995
Issue Price: £59.75

Code: CC934
Issued: April 1995 —
March 1996
Issue Price: £29.95

HAPPY FAMILY

Features Lally and Miles and their twins.

Club and limited Editions

BELLAMY
Issued: Feb 1995

Peter's sculpture is based on a real bear of the same name commissioned by Frances Fagan from Frank Webster of The House of Bruin in Loughborough. The bear was created out of a real fur cloak owned by Frances, and the purpose of Peter's Bellamy is to raise funds and public awareness about issues involving the conservation of wildlife and endangered species. During 1995 Bellamy will be made available exclusively to Collectors Club members; in 1996 the piece will join the main Colour Box range. He is named after Dr. David Bellamy, though his original working title was Big Bear.

ADDITIONAL ITEMS
BOOK MARKS
Issued: June 1992
A choice of six Colour Box book marks were introduced in 1992 as a free gift for Club members who enrol a friend. Each book mark features a tie-on animal. Since June and Christmas 1992 all book marks issued have been signed by Peter Fagan.

SET OF BOOKS

Robert (BK001), Bruno (BK002), Jonathan (BK003)
Issued: June 1992
Issue Price: £10
Three of Frances Fagan's books made available to Collectors Club members in an attractive slip cover. Initially a limited number were signed by the author, and during the 10th Anniversary year (1993) Frances also included special messages to collectors on request.

LIMITED EDITIONS
The following pieces have been issued by Colour Box in pre-announced limited editions.

Code: TCL01
Issued: Sept 1993
Edition Size: 1,500
Issue Price: £35

TEDDY BEARS' PICNIC

Produced to celebrate the tenth anniversary year of Colour Box and supplied with a numbered certificate. The edition sold out in a matter of weeks.

THE AUCTION ROOM

A special piece produced in a numbered edition of just 10 to commemorate Christie's first all teddy bear auction on 6th December 1993, which included 40 lots of Colour Box items. Ten of the lots were these very pieces. The auctioneer bear standing at the rostrum is Lord Paul (TC124), who is named after the Managing Director of Christie's, Paul Barthauld. Each version of The Auction Room is hand-painted differently: Number One has an ivory gavel, Number Two has a silver gavel; Lord Paul's tipple (hidden behind the rostrum) is different on every piece, so too are the selection of bears. However, all the bears featured on the pieces have one thing in common; they were purchased from Christie's by Peter and Frances Fagan. The rostrum is an accurate model of the famous Christie's rostrum; dating from1825 it is the oldest purpose built rostrum in the world. All the net profits from these lots were donated to the Child Accident Prevention Trust.

One of the pieces was subsequently stolen in transit to its Australian purchaser and Peter made another special piece as a replacement. The edition size was not compromised as he varied the piece from the original ten.

Code: None
Issued: December 1993
Retired: December 1993
Edition Size: 10
Issue Price: Between £900
and £1,050 at the
Christie's auction.

ALL AT SEA

Each piece is present-ed in a silk lined box and with a numbered certificate and base label. On board are Miranda, Adrian, Fluffy, Sullivan, Sopwith and Clarissa.

Code: TC 102
Issued: Sept 1994
Edition Size: 3,000
Issue Price: £50

THE SCHOOLROOM

Created exclusively for shops in the UK which are members of the Glass and China Guild.

Code: GD001
Issued: Oct 1994
Edition Size: 1,500
Issue Price: £49.95

Since 1988 Peter Fagan has created a number of Christmas sculptures, often featuring characters from other collections in festive surroundings. Needless to say they are amongst the most popular of all Colour Box creations.

CHRISTMAS HAMPER

The bear sitting in the hamper with the Christmas pudding and the champagne bottle is Peregrine and he was cast separately during production! The piece is marked © PF 89.

Code: XTC316
Issued: 1989
Retired: 1991
Issue Price: £8

CHRISTMAS MORNING

Fluffy, Bruno and Johann are the bears featured on this piece. All were cast separately and attached later.

Code: XTC003
Issued: 1989
Retired: 1991
Issue Price: £45

BOXING DAY ▶

Here August String-Bear can be seen amongst the leftovers of the Christmas Party. He really enjoyed pulling Christmas crackers and, although his hat was a bit big, he was very pleased with his little treasure, the dice that he found inside.

Although released in 1989, Peter sculpted this piece the year before, hence the marking: © 88 PF.

Code: XTC313
Issued: 1989
Retired: 1991
Issue Price: £7

CAROL SINGERS

Code: XTC004
Issued: 1990
Retired: 1993
Issue Price: £22

*J*ust about a week before Christmas the carol singers start to put everyone in the right frame of mind for this special time of year. In the back of the old village church everyone gathers on a cold dark evening hoping that some parishioners will have hot mince pies and a mug of tea for after the doorstep concert.

Master painter Terry Fairbairn remembers having great difficulty originating the colour of the pew and eventually went into Lauder Church (a few yards from the Colour Box studios) to look at the real thing before getting it just right. Before the name Carol Singers was decided upon, the piece was known just as "Pew". Dickie Bear on this piece is a 'glue-on' (cast separately), so too is Teddy Bear (H40) on the floor, a Hopscotch forerunner of the Teddy Bears collection proper.

LETTER TO SANTA ▶

*F*eaturing Fluffy, Peregrine, Robert and Dickie Bear.

Code: XTC002
Issued: 1990
Retired: 1991
Issue Price: £30

JACK IN THE BOX ▼

*S*anta popped this toy in Lucy Fagan's stocking one Christmas night and the following year Peter's model of it was in more than one little girl's stocking! Note the startled expression on Dickie Bear's face. A modified version of this piece (with the 'glue-on' Dickie Bear replaced by a Whistler mouse) was issued in 1994 in the USA as part of the Pennywhistle Lane collection.

CHRISTMAS SURPRISES ▼

*M*oved to Teddy Bear Collection as Birthday Surprises (TC118). Also remodelled without the Christmas trimmings and released in 1992 as Bartholomew (TC226).

Code: XTC317
Issued: 1990
Retired: 1993
Issue Price: £5.50

Code: XTC118
Issued: 1991
Retired: 1992
Issue Price: £13

Seasonal collection

MISTLETOE BEAR

Remodelled without the Christmas trimmings and released in 1992 as Emlyn (TC627).

Code: XTC218
Issued: 1991
Retired: 1993
Issue Price: £10

PRESENT TIME

The bear on this piece, minus the Christmas stocking and his collar, was released in 1992 as James and retired in 1993. Meanwhile Present Time in its unaltered state was reissued in 1994 in the USA as part of the Pennywhistle Lane collection and renamed James.

Code: XTC418
Issued: 1991
Retired: 1993
Issue Price: £5

Code: XTC419
Issued: 1991
Retired: 1993
Issue Price: £5

PARTY BEAR

Remodelled without the Christmas bits and pieces and released as Popsey in 1992. Like Present Time, Party Bear in its unaltered, original version was also reissued in 1994 in the USA as part of the Pennywhistle Lane collection and renamed Popsey.

Seasonal Collection

Other Items

THE WORLD CHAMPION

Code: BK004
Issued: 1991
Retired: 1993
Issue Price: £29.99

A bookend sculpted by Peter Fagan to complement the three books of Teddy stories written by Frances Fagan — Robert, Bruno and Jonathan — also issued in 1991.

THE EDWARD HARROD COLLECTION

Edward Harrod is a very old bear who was discovered in a cupboard in the famous London store that 'bears' his name. It is believed that for many years he belonged to Charles Digby Harrod, son of the founder of the store.

Each piece is accompanied by a story leaflet illustrated with an original photograph from the Harrods archive (remarkably Edward Harrod appears in every one!). The collection was launched with vast success at a promotion on 10th June 1992 — Harrods sold out their entire year's supply of two of the pieces in one day!

A complete set of the Edward Harrod Collection, signed by Mohammed Al Fayed, Chairman of Harrods, was donated by Harrods to the 1993 Christie's sale and fetched £198.

The Edward Harrod Collection is available exclusively from the Harrods store in London, Harrods International Stores, Harrods Airport shops and on the QE2. Two new pieces, not listed here, may be added to the collection during 1995.

THE FISH COUNTER

*T*he famous Harrods fish counter is a great attraction for an aristocratic bear who adores lobster, crab and shellfish of all kinds and, above all, caviar. The Fish Counter is a piece which master painter Terry Fairbairn particularly enjoyed working on. Using a photograph of the real thing for reference, she was able to perfect the colours first time.

Code: HTC001
Issued: June 1992
Issue Price: £39.95

HARRODS HAMPER

*H*arrods hampers are delivered all over the world, and Edward Harrod can remember the days before combustion engines when bicycles, horse and carts, and even steam traction engines were painted in the distinctive Harrods green livery.

Code: HTC002
Issued: June 1992
Issue Price: £19.95

Other Items

CRUISE LINER

*H*ere Edward Harrod is cast in the role of a nautical delivery boy, as Harrods prides itself on being able to order and deliver just about anything anywhere in the world — even a baby elephant (ordered by one Ronald Reagan, no less!). A further 'cruise liner' connection is the Harrods shop on the QE2.

Code: HTC003
Issued: June 1992
Issue Price: £19.95

DELIVERY BEAR

*A*n occasional treat for Edward is a trip on a Harrods delivery van, although these jaunts do not always pass off without mishap and once the van he was travelling in swerved off a country road and ended up in a ditch. "Rabbits!" was all Edward could hear his driver, Arthur, muttering. "There ought to be a law . . ."

Code: HTC004
Issued: June 1992
Issue Price: £10.95

Code: HTC005
Issued: June 1992
Issue Price: £10.95

HARRODS SHOPPER

*H*ere Edward visits one of the most genteel departments in the early days of the store's existence — the Children's Robe Room — and imagines himself as a foreign Arch-Duke or Russian Viscount.

Code: HTC006
Issued: June 1992
Issue Price: £10.95

TOP HAT AND TAILS

*H*arrods was the first store in the world to have a 'moving staircase' and, dressed suitably in top hat and tails, Edward watches ladies queuing up to enjoy this strange new experience.

PLAYTIME BEAR

*E*dward pops in to see the opening of the Harrods Toy Department. It occurs to him that one of the children might want to buy him; what would he do then? He silently crosses his toes and waits for them to move on!

Code: HTC007
Issued: June 1992
Retired: 1995
Issue Price: £8.95

Code: HTC008
Issued: June 1992
Issue Price: £8.95

SECOND CHEF

*M*ost bears have a passion for honey, but not Edward — he prefers chocolate and is only too happy to don a chef's hat if it means lingering in the kitchen at Harrods where hand made chocolates are made.

BOATER BEAR

*B*oaters are worn by the sales assistants in the Food Halls, where the fruit and flower displays are so impressive that Edward Harrod considers it a pity when customers come in and disturb the arrangements!

Code: HTC009
Issued: June 1992
Retired: 1995
Issue Price: £8.95

Code: HTC010
Issued: June 1992
Issue Price: £6.95

EDWARD HARROD

*H*aving been shut in a cupboard for so many years, Edward had no idea what the actual store looked like and when he eventually saw the facade for the first time, he was astonished. "Magnificent!" he gasped.

COMMISSIONAIRE BEAR

Launched at the same time as Pilgrim. The hat Peter used to model this piece belonged to a real Harrods Doorman, Rodney, and was donated by Harrods for the 1993 Christie's auction.

Code: HTC011
Issued: October 1992
Issue Price: £10.95

PILGRIM

A miniature of the 1992 Harrods Christmas Bear of the same name which reflects the store's seasonal theme for that year — New England Christmas. Available for one year only.

Code: HTC012
Issued: October 1992
Retired: October 1993
Issue Price: £8.95

OPENING BAT

Edward Harrod is called upon to revive the English hopes for the Ashes!

Code: HTC013
Issued: October 1994
Issue Price: £10.95

SHOPPING SPREE

Here our hero experiences the excitement of a Harrods sale.He peeps nervously from the safe haven of one of those famous green shopping bags as the crowds enter the store.

Code: HTC013
Issued: October 1994
Issue Price: £10.95

THE HERMANN 'FAMILY'

A collection of twelve bears sculpted from originals in the archives of the German bear manufacturer, Hermann. The collection is available exclusively from Debenhams in the UK and through the Colour Box distributor, Praesent Sterling, in Germany.

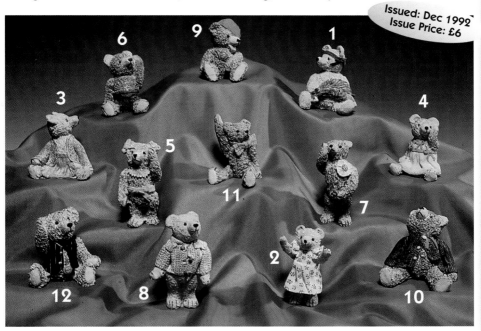

Issued: Dec 1992
Issue Price: £6

1. ANDREA	7. FRITZ
2. ANNA	8. HELLMUT
3. CHRISTINA	9. HERMANN
4. DOROTHEE	10. KARL
5. STEFANIE	11. WERNER
6. BERNHARD	12. SIR ARTHUR

THE LAWLEYS COLLECTION

A collection of four bears created for and available exclusively from Lawleys china and glass stores. Frances Fagan explains the strange circumstances under which the project began: *"Edgar Lawley has come to join Colour Box after a rather bizarre incident in Leek, Staffordshire!*

"On our way to having lunch with Rosemary Booth, the buyer for the Lawley's china and glass stores, we had a minor mishap and Peter ran into the back of her car! — Ooops! Peter made some awful joke about making a big impression on our best customers, but everyone else straightened up and were grateful that no one was hurt.

"Standing on the roadside waiting for the garage repair crew, we all regretted missing our pub lunch, when we were introduced to a passenger in Rosemary's car who we hadn't realised was really there.

"Edgar Lawley Bear had been catapulted onto the floor, but none the worse for his bump, was retrieved and introduced to Peter. There and then, on the kerbside, a new range was created. (Peter always was one for taking advantage of a situation!)"

Lawleys 94

Code: LC001
Issued: October 1994
Issue Price: £6.95

Code: LC002
Issued: October 1994
Issue Price: £11.50

Code: LC003
Issued: October 1994
Issue Price: £11.50

Code: LC004
Issued: October 1994
Issue Price: £9.50

1. CLOWNING AROUND
2. GIFT BOX BEAR
3. EDGAR LAWLEY
4. EDGAR'S SPECIAL DAY

BARCLAYCARD PROFILES

Sculptures by Peter Fagan are available to Barclaycard holders via their Profiles catalogue. Profiles is a loyalty scheme whereby points are accrued depending on the amount of purchases made using Barclaycard. Pieces from the current ranges of Teddies and Home Sweet Home are available (Story Time, Rabbit Hutch, On The Fence, Educating Timmy), and the option to purchase a year's membership to the Collectors Club. Barclaycard have also commissioned two pieces exclusively for their Profiles catalogue, Racing Ted and Cosy Kittens (Home Sweet Home collection), between May 1994 and May 1995.

Racing Ted
Issued: May 1994

Racing Ted does not have an issue price: Barclaycard holders require 600 Profile points to purchase the piece, and one point is awarded for every £10 charged on a Barclaycard.

BRITISH AIRWAYS BEARS

Colour Box were commissioned by British Airways to create three bears in BA uniforms for their in-flight duty free service. Pilot, Steward, Stewardess are sold as a boxed set for £12.50 and are not available individually.
The tone of the blue on the uniforms was darkened during pre-production after consultation with British Airways.

Pilot   Stewardess   Steward

TEDDY RANDELL

Teddy Randell belonged to a little girl called Sally-Ann who loved him dearly. When Sally-Ann became very poorly and had to go to hospital, Teddy Randell naturally went with her, until one day a nurse picked him up and carried him away to a quiet room. There he met a bear called Squidge and they became firm friends. Shortly afterwards they were both auctioned and came to live with Peter Fagan. [There is a great deal more fascinating detail to this story which Frances Fagan will hopefully narrate in full one day in book form.]

Teddy Randell miniatures were originally sculpted in 1991 to raise money for the Royal Hospital for Sick Children (known affectionately as "The Sick Kids") in Edinburgh and are painted with a number of colour variations to the heart badge. A set of Teddy Randell miniatures including all the paint variations was sold at the 1993 Christie's auction for £220.

Green Heart

Purple Heart

Code: STC01
Issued: 1991
Issue Price: £2.95
(regardless of heart colour)

Gold Heart

Two gold heart Teddy Randells exist. One was painted for the winner of the draw when the original Teddy Randell was taken up the height of Mount Everest on an exercise machine by athlete Sandy Cumming in aid of Charity. The other is the Colour Box archive copy which was auctioned at Christie's in 1993 and is signed by Sandy Cumming.

Green Heart
Issued: 8th September 1991
(for one day only)
Edition Size: 500

The Sick Kids appeal was launched at a Fun Day on 8th September at The Meadows, Edinburgh, where a special colourway of Teddy Randell with a green heart-shaped badge was available. All 500 were sold in less than an hour, and all the money taken was given to the hospital.

Pink or Blue Heart
Issued: September 1991

Teddy Randell with a choice of either a pink or a blue heart was also launched at the Fun Day and then made available to collectors through their stockists. For one year all profits from sales were given to The Sick Kids Fund. Eventually an impressive £10,000 was raised for the fund; the cheque was handed over in September 1992 on the occasion of Sopwith Bear's flight in an RAF Tornado.

Purple Heart
Issued: October 1991
Edition Size: 500

A limited edition colourway with a purple heart badge was produced to raise money for the Hilversum Babies Hospital in Holland, and sold at the Teddy Bear Festival in Soesterberg, near Utrecht.

COLOURWAYS

For a number of years prior to the introduction of special promotional pieces in 1993 (Miles, Travelling Cat, Promotional Pup), Colour Box created colourways of figurines from the current collections for limited sale at store promotions and other events. They include the following:

Baron Von Berne
(TC801)
Green and silver hat — produced for Lawleys Collectors Weekend, Apr 1993.

Bertram
(TC617)
Green scarf — an edition of just 50 was produced exclusively for the first and only Collectors Club Road Show held on 16th November 1990 in Dumfries. (Although the Road Show was a great success, further shows have not materialised as they are too time consuming for Colour Box to organise.)

Buster
(TC217)
1) Blue top with 'B' on breast pocket — produced for Blue Chip Travel in Edinburgh as a corporate gift, Christmas 1992.
2) Sage green top with 'N J B' on front — produced for Not Just Bears in New Zealand, Dec 1993.
3) Red and green top — produced for Lawley's, Reading, Oct 1993.

Bruno
(TC417)
Red & white scarf — produced for Lincoln Co-op, Oct 1993.

Bumble
(TC224)
Red & white scarf — produced for Lincoln Co-op, Oct 1993.

Chocolate Chip
(TC457)
Colourway — produced for Cottage Crafts, Sawbridgeworth, Sept 1992.

Derek
(TC800)
Red hat — presented as gifts to collectors who attended the Colour Box Collectors Club weekend at the Johnstoneburn House Hotel (near Lauder), April 1991.

Elly May
(TC632)
Brown bow and patterned coat — produced for Cameo House, Chesham, Jun 1994.

Fred
(TC465)
Colourway — produced for Choice, Welwyn, Sept 1993.

George
(TC619)
1) Red waistcoat — produced for Lawley's, initially for Christmas 1993 was not on sale until Jan 1994.
2) Green waistcoat with 'K & S' in gold letters — produced for Kirkcaldie & Staines, New Zealand.

Jilly Bear
(TC614)
Different coloured apron — produced for Owen Owen, Ilford, Oct 1992.
Prudence (TC625)
1) Red trim to hat and dress — produced for Glorious Britain, Gatwick Airport, July 1993.
2) Colourway — produced for Choice, Welwyn, Sept 1993.
3) Pink dress with white edging — produced for Lynn's Cards and Gifts, Woking, Nov 1993.

Stanley
(TC628)
Green and red waistcoat — produced for Randells, Wellingborough, Nov 1993.

Sullivan
(TC 328)
White/red & green with 'I'r Dim' on front — produced for Just Right, Denbigh, Sept 1993.

POINT OF SALE
BLACKBOARD

Code: CC87
Issued: March 1993
Issue Price: £7.99

Blackboard was originally issued back in 1984 as a point of sale for retailers to display in their shops. In those days, it had a second cat — Striped Cat (H1) — which was replaced by a teddy bear for relaunch in 1993. In its original form a version was also created for the USA using the transatlantic trading name 'Adorables'.

Blackboard has had yet a further incarnation — as the free joining gift to members of the 1987 Collectors Club.

PROMOTION PIECES

These pieces (three in all, one for each of the main collections) were specially designed to be painted with appropriate text as a souvenir of Colour Box promotions and replaced the idea of colourways of existing pieces. They are generally only available at a promotion, on the day, though retailers also mail out the pieces by prior arrangement if collectors cannot attend in person.

Certain detail on each piece is specially painted for each promotion and no two versions are alike. Colour Box give the shop hosting each promotion the opportunity to choose the colours of their own colourway.

MILES

Code No: STC04
Issued: September 1993
Issue Price: £6.50

Miles, the travelling Bear, was launched at the 1993 Hugglets Teddy Festival in London. (The following year he was secretly married to Lally.)
The front waistcoat and bow are painted differently for each promotion.

1995 COLOUR BOX EVENT PIECE

For Colour Box's Collectors Event in Spalding, Lincs, 13-14 May 1995, Peter Fagan has sculpted a special event piece - The Spalding Express - available only to collectors in person on the day(s). Further details of the piece had not been finalised as this book went to print.

'PANDA TWINS'

A new piece is being planned — a miniature of twin Pandas owned by the Fagans — to commemorate the opening of new premises for long-standing Colour Box stockist Clifton Collectables in Lancashire. The piece will be made available exclusively from Clifton Collectables from September 1995 onwards and then join the main Colour Box collection in spring 1996.

THE STEIFF COLLECTION

A Collection of teddies based on bears from the Steiff factory museum in Giengen/Brenz, Germany. The pieces are marketed by the Steiff company and not by Colour Box, and there are currently three in the range.

1. Teddy Rose & Bully Hund
Issued: Spring 1994

The original Teddy Rose was made in 1925. The rose colouring of this teddy was unusual for the 1920s. His nose and claws are hand-stitched. His friend is Bully Dog who was originally made in 1927. He has a stitched muzzle and claws and round his neck he sports a studded leather collar with a bell. Teddy Rose is holding Bully almost as if to make sure he doesn't bound off in any direction for some fun.

2. Bearle & Rolly Drolly
Issued: Spring 1994

The original Bearle is a 1904 Steiff bear with a sealing wax nose with string fastened discs on his limbs. He has an appealing, inquisitive face which encourages any collector to pick him up. The plush Rolly Drolly is a get-up clown made of mohair and stuffed with wood shavings. The face, hands and neck collar are made of felt and the arms and head are movable. This colourful clown goes back as far as 1909.

3. Zotty & Tiger
Issued: Spring 1994

The original Zotty dates from 1951, is 14" high and is made of long-mohair plush and stuffed with soft man-made fibre. The tiger is slightly younger, dating from 1955 and is made of mohair with sophisticated colouring.

Also . . .

Steiff Bear
Produced by Colour Box in a limited edition and presented to their customers (i.e. stockists) at the 1991 Nurnberg Toy Fair, Germany.

Steiff Clown
Presented to Colour Box customers at the 1992 Nurnberg Toy Fair, Germany.

Rare & Unreleased Items

ALFONZO

The real Alfonzo is rather famous. He belonged to a Russian princess and once reached a world record price at a Christie's auction. He now lives at a shop called Teddy Bears in Witney, Oxfordshire. In 1993 Colour Box created a miniature of him in a limited edition of 2,000 (now sold out). He cost £6 and was available exclusively from Teddy Bears of Witney. Peter Fagan sculpted the piece (pictured here) in a sitting position from a photograph of Alfonzo. He has now sculpted a second version, this time standing, using the original as his model. This new piece is also available exclusively from Teddy Bears of Witney at a cost of £10 in an unlimited edition. TEDDY BEARS, 99 High Street, Witney, Oxfordshire OX8 6LY
Tel: (01993) 702616 Fax: (01993) 702344

BIZZY LIZZY

Bizzy Lizzy was modelled in 1993 but never released as it was too small to demould intact from the moulds on a production run. As with Merton, the original and the unique miniature master were sold at the 1993 Christie's auction.
Auction Price: £198 (pair)

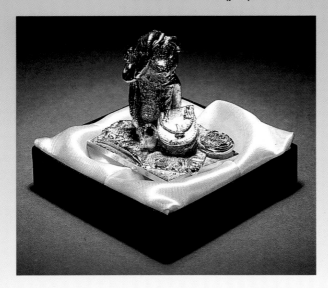

GOLDEN BEAR

A 1/1 Limited Edition of Highland Laddie was cast in solid gold for a promotion at a trade show in Harrogate, July 1988. Names of Colour Box customers (i.e. stockists) who attended the show were entered in a draw and this unique and very valuable piece was won by the Alresford Gift Shop in Hampshire. At the time the 'Golden Bear' created quite a bit of media interest as it was the largest piece of solid gold to be cast in Scotland for more than a century.

JOHNSON BEAR ▶

When Bear With Us opened in 1991 in Lichfield, Staffordshire, the shop commissioned a house bear, Johnson, and the following year Peter Fagan created a miniature of him for sale exclusively from Bear With Us. Johnson, a limited edition of 1,000, is still available at £7.99. He is named after Dr Johnson, who was born and bred in Lichfield.
BEAR WITH US 41 Tamworth Street, Lichfield, Staffordshire
Tel: (01543) 250410

LITTLE ARCHIE

Archie was one of the first bears created by Joan Bland, founder of 'Asquiths', the UK's first Teddy Bear shop in Windsor, Berkshire. The original was available in two sizes, and no prizes for guessing which one Peter Fagan sculpted! When Joan saw Peter's 'master' she was amazed at the accuracy with which he had captured the original and not a single alteration was required. Little Archie was released in 1992 in a limited edition of 2,000 and is still available exclusively from 'Asquiths' (there are now three shops: Windsor, Eton, Henley-on-Thames) at £6.95. For more information please contact:
ASQUITHS 2-4 New Street, Henley-on-Thames, Oxfordshire RG9 2LF
Tel: (01491) 571978   Fax: (0491) 577363

MERTON ▶

Facially, Merton, a real bear, closely resembles Brodie and although the model Peter made is not similar to Colour Box Brodie, their features were too alike and it was decided not to launch Merton. The plush original and the unique miniature master were both sold at the Christie's teddy auction in December 1993.
1993 Auction Price: £187 (pair)

NOEL ▼

A 1/1 Limited Edition commissioned by Christie's for a charity auction held on 5th December 1994 to raise money for Children In Need. The piece is large by Colour Box standards (more than 7 inches high) and was presented in a special box with handwritten certificate.

TEDDY ROYALE ▶

T eddy Royale was commissioned by Pottery Plus of Chelmsley Wood, Birmingham, to help raise money for the Birmingham Children's Hospital Appeal — for every piece sold £1 goes to the fund. Peter's scultpure is based upon the hospital's mascot and was produced in a limited edition of 2,000. The piece was launched at a promotion on 9th October 1993 — issue price £10.95. Teddy Royale is still currently available.
POTTERY PLUS 20 Maple Walk,
Chelmsley Wood,
Birmingham
Tel: (0121) 770 9930

PLAYTIME TEDS

A collection of nine pieces modelled by Peter early in the development of Colour Box which were never released commercially. Twelve were sold at the Christie's auction as one lot.
1993 Auction Price: £198 (set of 12)

SOPWITH PROTOTYPE ▼

S opwith as you've never seen him before! This is how Peter Fagan originally sculpted the piece, but the poor bear was none too happy immortalised doing the 'splits' and was restyled with both feet forward before released in 1990.

M e m o r a b i l i a

This section includes details of some ranges which include both Teddy and Home Sweet Home characters.

BOOKS

Three books inspired by the original Colour Box bears of the same name, written by Frances Fagan as told to Peter's youngest daughter, Lucy.

ROBERT
Code: BK001
Issued: 1991
Issue Price: £2.95

JONATHAN
Code: BK003
Issued: 1991
Issue Price: £2.95

BRUNO
Code: BK002
Issued: 1991
Issue Price: £2.95

The Robert, Bruno and Jonathan books were also offered exclusively to Club members in a slip cover in 1992 (see Collectors Club).

PICTURES

Commissioned portraits of some of the Teddies and Home Sweet Home Collections depicting scenes from their lives. The pictures are the work of artists Deidre Mackay-Clark (Teddies) and Julie Jones (Home Sweet Home). They are framed under glass in high-quality mounts. Three of them — Robert and Dickie, Jilly and Bernard, Bruno and Teddy Robinson — are signed limited editions.
(N.B. All Pictures, including Home Sweet Home characters, are listed.)

Nursery Time
Code: PS11
Issued: 1990
Issue Price: £7.75

Shelf-life
Code: PS12
Issued: 1990
Issue Price: £7.75

The Listener
Code: PS13
Issued: 1990
Issue Price: £7.75

Washday Blues
Code: PS14
Issued: 1990
Issue Price: £7.75

Home Cooking
Code: PS15
Issued: 1990
Issue Price: £7.75

Robert and Dickie
(Limited Edition)

Festive Fun
Code: PS16
Issued: 1990
Issue Price: £7.75

Fishermans Friend
Code: PS17
Issued: 1990
Issue Price: £7.75

Theodore
Code: PS21
Issued: 1990
Issue Price: £12.99

Johann
Code: PS22
Issued: 1990
Issue Price: £12.99

Jonathan
Code: PS23
Issued: 1990
Issue Price: £12.99

The Listener
Code: PL13
Issued: 1990
Issue Price: £12.99

Washday Blues
Code: PL14
Issued: 1990
Issue Price: £12.99

Home Cooking
Code: PL15
Issued: 1990
Issue Price: £12.99

Fishermans Friend
Code: PL17
Issued: 1990
Issue Price: £12.99

Peregrine, Sopwith and Ralph
Code: PT001
Issued: July 1990
Issue Price: £14.99

Johann, Jonathan and Theodore
Code: PT002
Issued: July 1990
Issue Price: £14.99

Leftovers
Code: PS18
Issued: July 1990
Issue Price: £12.99

Party Capers
Code: PS19
Issued: July 1990
Issue Price: £12.99

Peregrine
Code: PS24
Issued: July 1990
Issue Price: £12.99

Ralph
Code: PS25
Issued: July 1990
Issue Price: £12.99

Sopwith
Code: PS26
Issued: 1990
Issue Price: £12.99

Christopher
Code: PS27
Issued: 1991
Issue Price: £13.75

Peter
Code: PS28
Issued: 1991
Issue Price: £13.75

Gustav von Bruin
Code: PS29
Issued: 1991
Issue Price: £13.75

Robert and Dickie
(Limited Edition)
Code: PEL1
Issued: 1990
Edition Size: 950
Issue Price: £39.95
All pictures in the edition are signed by the artist.

Jilly and Bernard
(Limited Edition)
Code: PEL2
Issued: July 1990
Edition Size: 999
Issue Price: £39.95
All pictures in the edition are signed by the artist.

Bruno and Teddy Robinson
(Limited Edition)
Code: PEL3
Issued: 1991
Edition Size: 999
Issue Price: £39.95

CARDS

Greetings cards with designs based upon the 'Picture' illustrations by Deidre Mackay-Clark.

Issued: 1990
Theodore (CA001), Jonathan (CA002), Johann (CA003), Peregrine (CA004), Sopwith (CA005), Ralph (CA006).

Issued: 1991
Christopher (CA007), Peter(CA008), Gustav Von Bruin (CA009), "In the chair reserved for bears, sat Bruno!" (CA010), "Then he'd find himself on the rostrum above the other competitors" (CA011) "And Robert watched over her all night long" (CA012), "And they all lived happily ever after" (CA013), "He'd understand how she felt" (CA014), "Pick him up gently and take him upstairs" (CA201). Cards CA010 to CA201 feature illustrations from Frances Fagan's books — Robert, Bruno, Jonathan — which were photographs adapted by an in-house Colour Box artist from Frances' brief.

COLOUR BOX ANTICS

Illustrations of cats by Julie Jones.
Issued: late 1991
Nursery Time (CA201), The Listeners (CA202), Washday Blues (CA203, Four Friends (CA204), Party Capers (CA205, Sitting Pretty (CA206).

PEEPSHOW

Issued: late 1991
Festive Fun (CA101, Home Cooking (CA102), Washday Blues (CA103),
Shelf Life (CA104), The Listeners (CA105), The Attic (CA106).

SWEATSHIRTS AND TEE-SHIRTS

Issued: Spring 1990
Issue Price: £14.95 (Sweatshirt)/£7.50 (Tee-shirt).
Sweatshirts in navy blue (50%cotton 50% polyester)
Tee-shirts in white (100% cotton)
Both with the Colour Box logo printed on the front.
Available in three sizes — Small, Medium and Large.

CERAMICS

Fine bone china featuring Colour Box Cats and Bears. All items supplied in customised presentation boxes.

Nursery Set

Code: CB51
Issued: 1990
Issue Price: £17.50
Three piece set (bowl, plate, mug) depicting the cats playing with Lucy's rocking horse in the nursery.

Washday Set

Code: CB53
Issued: 1990
Issue Price: £17.50
Three piece set (bowl, plate, mug) depicting the cats working in the kitchen on washday.

Four Friends Set

Code: CB53
Issued: 1990
Issue Price: £17.50
Three piece set (bowl, plate, mug) — also sold separately — depicting the four bears from the Curios Shop surrounded by toys.

The Listener Mug

Code: CM4
Issued: 1991
Issue Price:

Sitting Pretty Mug

Code: CM5
Issued: 1991
Issue Price:

Party Capers Mug

Code: CM6
Issued: 1991
Issue Price:

DEAN'S RAG BOOK REPLICAS

The oldest teddy bear makers in Britain, Dean's Rag Book Company, have reproduced several favourite bears from the Colour Box collection in mohair, all in numbered limited editions:

Bertram

Issued: June 1992
Issue Price: £99.95
Edition Size: 500
The protoype sold at the 1993 Christie's auction for £242. The lot included a signed Colour Box master miniature and a variation colourway of the same bear.

Prudence

Issued: September 1992
Issue Price: £79.00
Edition Size: 800
The final bear of the edition (No. 800) was sold at the 1993 Christie's auction for £286. The lot included a signed Colour Box miniature of the same bear.

Chocolate Chip

Issued: September 1992
Issue Price: £48.00
Edition Size: 800
The final bear of the edition (No. 800) was sold at the 1993 Christie's auction for £165. The lot included a signed Colour Box miniature of the same bear.

Jonathan

Issued: September 1992
Issue Price: £27.00
Edition Size: 1,000
The final bear of the edition (No. 1,000) was sold at the 1993 Christie's auction for £154. The lot included a signed Colour Box miniature of the same bear.

Morris Minor

Issued: June 1993
Issue Price: £89.00
Edition Size: 1,000
The protoype sold at the 1993 Christie's auction for £264. The lot included a signed Colour Box miniature of the same bear.

Binkie

Issued: March 1994
Edition Size: 1,000

Lord Paul

A Limited Edition of just five Lord Paul mohair bears (replicas of the original bear owned by Peter Fagan) were created in 1993 to commemorate the Christie's teddy bear auction. One was presented to Christie's themselves and another to the Child Accident Prevention Trust. Two more were consigned to the Deans Ragbook and Colour Box archives. The fifth bear, complete with letter of authenticity, special certificate and handturned auctioneer's gavel signed by Lord Paul's namesake, Paul Barthauld (Managing Director of Christie's) was sold as one of the lots in the auction for £792.

Paisley

A bear in a Christmas stocking, available only for 25 days — December 1993.

Adrian

Issued: September 1994
Issue Price: £59.99
Edition Size: 1,000
In 1994 Deans also launched a range of PVC items featuring Colour Box bears: 2 x bags and an apron in two sizes (child + adult).

LAPEL PINS

Issued: March 1994
Issue Price: £1.95

A Colour Box lapel pin featuring the Colour Box logo.

CALENDAR

Issued: September 1994
Issue Price: £5.75

A 1995 Calendar available exclusively for Collectors Club members and their friends, featuring hand-painted scenes by Linda Lovatt.

COLOUR BOX VIDEO

Issued: Dec 1994
Issue Price: £12.99

A 45 minute video featuring (amongst other things)how the miniatures are made, in-store promotions and painting demonstrations, Sopwith's solo flight (the real thing!), the 1993 Christie's auction, and Colour Box staff and collectors.

Colour Box 1995 calendar

Colour Box 1995 lapel pin

OTHER ITEMS MADE UNDER LICENSE

ELITE GIFT BOXES
Tons of teddies on tins, including lunch boxes and pencil cases.

In December 1993 a special Christmas offer of a selection of Elite Teddy Tins with a brooch from Handcast inside were made via the Collectors Club (Issue price: £6.95 each).

At the 1993 Christie's auction, a lot consisting of original artwork by Linda Lovett, used for the Elite Gift Box products, fetched £88.

JOHN ELLAM PICTURES
A range of de'coupage pictures showing scenes from the lives of the teddies.

GRUMBRIDGE
The familiar Home Sweet Home settings in gift tinware.

HANDCAST DESIGNS
A range of hand painted resin giftware, including picture frames and pot pourri boxes, featuring Prudence, Captain Arthur Crown, Morris Minor, Tick Tock Ted, Arabella and Grandma Rosie. They have also produced a range of brooches and ear-rings, and badges based upon the pot pourri box lids. Also from Handcast Designs . . .

Tick Tock Ted Clock
A Limited Edition of 500 painted in a special colour way for Collectors Club members, each one signed by the craftsman who made it.
Issued: 1993
Issue Price: £29.95

MELAMASTER
A range of melamine trays with scenes from the lives of the bears.

PERSPECTIVE PHOTOGRAPHICS
A range of colour postcards, depicting the original plush Colour Box Bears with stories on the reverse of each card to introduce the teddy characters.
Issue Price of all three sets: £9.95

Set No.1
Issued: September 1992
16 Postcards of Colour Box Teddies presented in a red silk wallet. Sets available to Collectors Club members included a message from Peter on the reverse of one of the cards.

Set No.2
Issued: March 1993
A further set of 16 Postcards featuring different Colour Box Teddies, this time in a yellow silk wallet.

Set No.3
Issued: March 1994
Eight notecards with sepia photographs of real cats, with envelopes, presented in a wallet.

An album containing a complete set of postcards, a photograph of Captain Arthur Crown showing his telescope (framed and glazed), and a miniature master of Captain Arthur crown were sold as one lot at Christie's in 1993 and fetched £165.

QUEEN'S CHINA
A range of nursery china portraying favourite teddies.
Gold Rimmed China Plate
Two Limited Edition plates have so far been produced and made available via the Collectors Club. The first one, issued in September 1993 in an edition of 500, sold out in just four days! The second plate, issued in November 1994, is available in an edition of 1,000.

A complete set of the Queen's China, the prototype of the Colour Box Collectors Club Limited Edition plate and the original artwork used in creating images for Colour Box Licensees, by Linda Lovatt, were sold as one lot at the 1993 Christie's auction for £132.

A lot consisting of other original artwork, by Linda Lovatt, used for stationery and tinware and the original artwork for the 1992 Colour Box Collectors Club Christmas card fetched £99.

Secondary Market Price Guide

Listed here are the prices at which retired Colour Box Teddy Bears originally sold when first released in the UK (First Issue Price) and an estimate of their current values on the secondary market. First Issue Prices from 1992 onwards are based on Colour Box's Recommended Retail Price Lists; prior to 1991, retailers set their own prices and these have been reconstructed approximately from details of Colour Box's trade prices. Current valuations are quoted both in UK pounds and US dollars using an exchange rate of 1.6 dollars to the pound.

It must be stressed that the valuations given are intended as a guide only and should be regarded as such. They have been compiled by the publishers and are current at the time of publication. Their sources include information gleaned from collectors and dealers whenever possible, and elsewhere by taking details of availability prior to retirement into consideration.

Collectors selling to dealers should be prepared to deduct anything from 15% to 50% from the prices quoted — 40% is probably an acceptable working average. Higher prices are paid for pieces in perfect condition and in their original box with accompanying leaflets.

Bronze Age Limited wish to point out that in line with their policy of non-involvement in secondary market, the prices quoted in this book were researched solely by the publishers.

NAME	CODE	ISSUE DATE	FIRST ISSUE PRICE £	CURRENT VALUE £ $
TOYBOX	TC110	1988	13.00	40-50 / 65-80
FISHERMANS FRIEND	TC111	1989	14.00	40-50 / 65-80
WRITING HOME	TC112	1990	12.00	25-30 / 40-50
BATHING BEACH	TC113	1990	12.00	30-35 / 50-55
STARCH AND PRESS	TC114	1990	19.95	40-45 / 65-75
FIRST AID POST	TC116	1991	16.99	
Red Cross				50-60 / 80-95
Green Cross				30-40 / 50-65
BIRTHDAY SURPRISES	TC118	1992	13.00	25-35 / 40-55
GRANDMA ROSIE	TC120	1992	12.99	15-25 / 25-40
HOLIDAY BEAR	TC210	1988	9.50	20-30 / 35-50
HOME MOVIES	TC211	1989	9.50	35-45 / 55-75
TRAIN SPOTTER	TC212	1990	10.00	20-30 / 35-50
TUCKBOX	TC213	1990	10.00	20-30 / 35-50
BAKING DAY	TC214	1990	10.00	20-30 / 35-50
NIGHT AT THE OPERA	TC215	1990	10.00	20-30 / 35-50
FLYING ACE	TC216	1983	10.00	20-30 / 35-50
BUSTER	TC217	1991	9.75	15-25 / 25-40
BENJI	TC220	1992	9.99	20-30 / 35-50
PEMBERTON	TC221	1992	9.99	20-30 / 35-50
MIRANDA	TC223	1992	9.99	20-30 / 35-50
BUMBLE	TC224	1992	9.99	15-25 / 25-40
JEROME	TC225	1992	9.99	15-25 / 25-40
BARTHOLOMEW	TC226	1992	9.99	20-30 / 35-50
HIGHLAND LADDIE	TC310	1988	8.75	20-30 / 35-50

NAME	CODE	ISSUE DATE	FIRST ISSUE PRICE £	CURRENT VALUE £ $
THE ACADEMIC	TC311	1988	8.75	30-40 / 50-65
LAP OF LUXURY	TC312	1988	8.00	30-40 / 50-65
ARTISTIC LICENCE	TC314	1989	8.99	30-40 / 50-65
THE QUIET LIFE	TC315	1989	17.50	45-55 / 75-90
EDUCATING TIMMY	TC316	1991	14.50	20-30 / 35-50
REGINA	TC324	1992	4.99	15-25 / 25-40
RAZZA	TC325	1992	4.99	15-25 / 25-40
BEATRICE	TC326	1992	4.99	15-25 / 25-40
SULLIVAN	TC328	1992	4.99	15-25 / 25-40
PHILIP	TC329	1992	4.99	15-25 / 25-40
RED BEAR	TC330	1992	4.99	20-30 / 35-50
ROBERT	TC411	1988	2.99	10-15 / 15-25
AUGUST STRING-BEAR	TC412	1988	2.99	10-15 / 15-25
GUSTAV VON BRUIN	TC413	1988	2.99	10-15 / 15-25
DICKIE BEAR	TC414	1988	2.99	10-15 / 15-25
HUMPHREY	TC416	1989	3.50	10-15 / 15-25
RALPH	TC418	1990	2.50	10-15 / 15-25
SOPWITH	TC419	1990	2.50	10-15 / 15-25
KLIM	TC422	1992	9.99	35-45 / 55-75
IRVINE	TC453	1991	2.99	10-15 / 15-25
SHINER	TC458	1991	2.99	10-15 / 15-25
POPSEY	TC463	1992	2.99	10-15 / 15-25
JAMES	TC464	1992	2.99	10-15 / 15-25
PEREGRINE	TC510	1988	1.75	5-10 / 8-15
THEODORE	TC512	1988	1.99	5-10 / 8-15
JOHANN	TC513	1988	1.99	5-10 / 8-15
MINI-MIDGE	TC609	1992	1.49	5-10 / 8-15
FLUFFY	TC610	1988	1.15	5-10 / 8-15
JONATHAN	TC611	1988	1.15	5-10 / 8-15
BRODERICK	TC612	1990	4.00	10-15 / 15-25
BERNARD	TC613	1990	4.00	10-15 / 15-25
JILLY BEAR	TC614	1990	5.00	10-15 / 15-25
ROGER	TC615	1990	5.00	10-15 / 15-25
TIMMY	TC616	1990	5.00	10-15 / 15-25
JIMMY	TC618	1991	4.85	10-15 / 15-25
DAMIEN		1991	4.85	
Red Coat	TC621			10-15 / 15-25
Blue Coat	TC622			10-15 / 15-25
Turquoise Coat	TC623			10-15 / 15-25
WILLIAM	TC624	1992	5.99	15-25 / 25-40
CLARISSA	TC626	1992	5.99	15-25 / 25-40
EMLYN	TC627	1992	5.99	15-25 / 25-40
BARROW BOY	TC700	1991	29.00	70-90 / 115-145
OH! MR PORTER	TC701	1991	29.00	70-90 / 115-145
DEREK	TC800	1991	4.85	10-15 / 15-25
BRODIE	TC802	1991	4.85	10-15 / 15-25
TEDDY RANDELL	STC01	1991	2.95	
Green Heart				25-35 / 40-55
Pink or Blue Heart				15-20 / 25-35
Purple Heart				25-35 / 40-55

NAME	CODE	ISSUE DATE	FIRST ISSUE PRICE £	CURRENT VALUE £ $	
COLLECTORS CLUB & LIMITED EDITIONS					
BLACKBOARD	CC87	1987	Nil	60-70 / 95-115	
EASEL	None	1988	Nil	60-70 / 95-115	
ATTIC	None	1989	Nil	60-70 / 95-115	
NOTICE BOARD	None	1990	Nil	55-65 / 90-100	
WALL	None	1991	Nil	40-50 / 65-80	
CHALKBOARD	None	1992	Nil	40-50 / 65-80	
BILLBOARD	None	1993	Nil	30-40 / 50-80	
THEODORE'S PASTIMES	None	1990	12.00	75-85 / 120-135	
SILVER MINIATURES		1989		————	
Mini Teddy	(H40)		21.00	90-100 / 145-160	
Cat & Ball	(H56)		25.00	90-100 / 145-160	
LIFEGUARD	None	1991	6.95	40-50 / 65-80	
TIME FOR REFLECTION	None	1991	20.95	70-90 / 115-145	
OUT FOR A RUN	None	1992	10.95	50-60 / 80-95	
SAIL AWAY	CC931S	1993	19.99	75-85 / 120-135	
SOPWITH'S SOLO FLIGHT	CC932S	1994	59.75	90-120 / 145-135	
THE AUCTION ROOM	None	1993	900 / 1,050	2,000+ / 3,200+	
SEASONAL COLLECTION					
LETTER TO SANTA	XTC002	1990	30.00	80-100 / 130-160	
CHRISTMAS MORNING	XTC003	1989	45.00	100-130 / 160-210	
CAROL SINGERS	XTC004	1990	22.00	75-85 / 120-135	
CHRISTMAS SURPRISES	XTC118	1991	13.00	45-55 / 75-90	
MISTLETOE BEAR	XTC218	1991	10.00	40-50 / 65-80	
BOXING DAY	XTC313	1989	7.00	35-45 / 55-75	
CHRISTMAS HAMPER	XTC316	1989	8.00	35-45 / 55-75	
JACK IN THE BOX	XTC317	1990	5.50	25-35 / 40-55	
PRESENT TIME	XTC418	1991	5.00	25-35 / 40-55	
PARTY BEAR	XTC419	1991	5.00	25-35 / 40-55	

Some Useful Addresses

COLOUR BOX COLLECTORS CLUB

If you are not already a member of the Colour Box Collectors Club please contact Vera Huber or Frances Fagan for an application form:
COLOUR BOX COLLECTORS CLUB
Colour Box Miniatures Limited
Orchard Estate
Lauder
Berwickshire TD2 6RH
Scotland
Tel: (0578) 722780

COLOUR BOX SHOP AND VISITORS CENTRE

The Colour Box shop is located in the Old Smiddy in Lauder and is open from 10am to 4pm Monday to Thursday and 10am to 3.30pm Fridays. You can also arrange to tour the factory and studios but only by prior appointment. Tours run on Tuesdays and Thursdays and begin from the shop at 10.30am. To book a tour please contact Pat Learmont, shop and showroom manageress, at the same address as above or Tel: (0578) 722725.

BUYING AND SELLING

For buying and selling retired collectables, the following magazines and newspapers are an established means of reaching dealers or placing classified advertisements:

EXCHANGE & MART
Link House
25 West Street, Poole, Dorset, England
Tel: (0202) 671171

CANADIAN COLLECTIBLES
(Formerly 'Insight on Collectibles')
103 Lakeshore Road Suite 262,
St Catherines, Ontario L2N 2T6 (Canada)
Canada's only collectibles publication

COLLECTORS MART
650 Westdale Drive, Wichita, Kansas 67209 (USA)
Bimonthly, dedicated to collectibles. Has a regular classified section featuring ads for dealers, including many secondary market listings.

TEDDY BEAR MAGAZINES

HUGGLETS
P.O. Box 290, Brighton BN2 1DR
Tel: (01273) 697974
A quarterly magazine dedicated to the world of teddy bears. Available on subscription at £12 for four copies from. Hugglets also organise a number of teddy bear shows.

TEDDY BEAR TIMES
Avalon Court, Star Road, Partidge Green, West Sussex RH13 8RY
Bi-monthly publication covering all aspects of teddy bears from the fun side to the more serious business of collecting. Price: £3.50 per issue or £21 annual subscription.

ALSO AVAILABLE FROM COLLECTABLES PUBLISHING LIMITED . . .

A COLLECTORS GUIDE TO DAVID WINTER COTTAGES
Softback: £19.95/$29.95
Hardback: £24.95/$39.95

A COLLECTORS GUIDE TO MYTH AND MAGIC
Softback: £19.95 Hardback: £25.95

COLLECTABLES PUBLISHING LIMITED
3 East Street, Littlehampton, West Sussex BN17 6AU
Tel: (01903) 733199 Fax: (01903) 733244

Index

(Main Teddy Bears collection only listed individually)

Index